PHYSICAL GEOGRAPHY OF INDIA

PHYSICAL GEOGRAPHY
OF INDIA

Prof. C. S. PICHAMUTHU

Professor of Geology, Bangalore University

NATIONAL BOOK TRUST, INDIA
NEW DELHI

December 1967 (Pausa 1889)

© *C. S. Pichamuthu, 1967*

Rs. 8.25

PUBLISHED BY THE SECRETARY, NATIONAL BOOK TRUST, INDIA, NEW DELHI-13
AND PRINTED AT THE NATIONAL PRINTING WORKS, 10 DARYAGANJ, DELHI-6.

FOREWORD

THIS is another addition to the Series that the National Book Trust has planned on "India—the Land and People".

The origin of the Series is the result of a discussion that I had with the late Prime Minister, Pandit Jawaharlal Nehru. When I first put the idea before him, he not only heartily approved it but gave many suggestions for making it more complete and attractive. It was his opinion that such a Series of books on India will form a permanent library of knowledge on every aspect of this country and is sure to make constructive contribution for national advancement in knowledge and education.

The Series proposes to cover every aspect of the country and will deal with its geography, geology, botany, zoology, agriculture, anthropology, culture, language, etc. Its ultimate aim is to create a kind of comprehensive library of books on India. We have endeavoured to have the books written by acknowledged authorities on various subjects and in a scientific way. Every effort is being made to see that they are easily understandable by the ordinary educated reader. The factual knowledge regarding the various subjects concerning India would be available to any ordinary reader who is not a specialist and who would like to have a knowledge of the subject in a relatively simple language.

We have been fortunate in getting the guidance of leading experts and scientists in various fields for this Project. In fact without their active co-operation it would not have been possible to plan the Series. We are thankful to our Board of Honorary Editors who are eminent specialists and leaders in their field for helping us in producing these volumes for the benefit of the ordinary reader.

In this book, Prof. C. S. Pichamuthu has presented India's Geography from the physical point of view explaining the formations and features so as to be easily understood by the common reader. Prof. Pichamuthu has long experience in the field of Geology and Geography. He has already written several papers on various aspects of Geomorphology, Geology and Mineralogy.

New Delhi;   B. V. KESKAR
September 22, 1967

CONTENTS

ACKNOWLEDGEMENTS

The publishers are grateful to the following for the photographs loaned to them:

Director-General, Survey of India;
Department of Geology, Bangalore University;
Prof. S. C. Chatterjee; and
Central Arid Zone Research Institute.

CHAPTER I

INTRODUCTION

GEOGRAPHY IS THE SCIENCE of the surface of the earth and its inhabitants. Of its many branches we are now concerned with *physical geography* which deals with those aspects of the earth which determine or influence the life of man. It necessarily touches other departments of natural knowledge at many points. Such contributory sciences are astronomy, geology, meteorology and physics.

Astronomical geography is concerned with map-making and the consideration of the earth as a planet. *Physical geology* is closely connected with the study of the materials and structure of the earth, the configuration of the earth's surface and the internal and external forces which have served to modify the earth through geological time. *Meteorological* factors influence the movements of the atmosphere and the hydrosphere, and consequently cause variations in weather and climate.

Physical geography or *physiography* includes the study of the atmosphere, water, and land-forms of the earth. In this sense it is somewhat more broad based than *geomorphology* which deals with the surface of the lithosphere, explaining its origin and interpreting its history. Geomorphology is closely related to geography but with this distinction that the geographer takes the earth features as they are and uses them as important components of man's physical environment, whereas the geomorphologist is primarily interested in the origin of these land-forms.

While it is possible to take for granted the infinite variety of landscape and scenery present on the earth's surface, appreciation of these natural phenomena is greatly enhanced if the agencies responsible for producing them are recognised, and the processes involved in their creation understood. It is necessary, therefore, not only to describe superficially the common surface features of the earth but to seek information as to their origin and development.

The earth on which we live is roughly spheroidal in shape and slightly flattened at the poles. The surface of the earth is not smooth but rises up in some places to form mountains and in others sinks below the depths of the seas. Most of the dry land is grouped together in seven large *continents* separated by vast *oceans*.

The earth is believed to be composed of a number of concentric shells of different densities surrounding a liquid core. The *crust* of the earth is the outermost solid shell which lies above the *mantle*. The crust itself is composed of a lighter upper zone (sial) composed essentially of rocks of a granitic composition, and a heavier lower zone (sima) formed of basalt. A thin and discontinuous layer of *sedimentary rocks* lies on the surface of the crust; overlying this is a discontinuous layer of water (oceans, seas and lakes) known as the *hydrosphere*. Surrounding everything is the gaseous envelope known as the *atmosphere*.

The continents are huge masses of sial floating, as it were, on the underlying sima. The real borders of the continents are not the present shorelines but the edges of the sialic blocks which extend for some distance under the seas. These submarine extensions form the *continental shelf*, which slope gently seaward. The outer margin of the continental shelf ends at what is known as the *continental slope*—the real limit of the sialic block—which steepens abruptly downwards into the floor of the *ocean basins*.

When we consider the highest parts of the continents and the deepest parts of the oceans, it is found that they both have an elongated shape. The mountains are in linear belts and made up of folded and faulted beds suggesting intensive earth-movements; they lie in what are known as *mobile belts*. Outside the mobile belts, the continental areas are comparatively more *stable*.

An interesting question concerns the *permanence* of continents and oceans, *i.e.* whether the main continental blocks and ocean basins have remained fixed in position throughout the long period of geological history. There is considerable evidence that the higher continental sialic masses have glided over the heavier substratum of sima and mantle, and changed places both in relation to their locations as well as to the poles. About 300 million years ago all the continents are supposed to have formed one large mass known as *Pangaea*. The term *Gondwanaland* is applied to the continental sheet in the southern hemisphere which comprised Africa, South America, Antarctica, Australia, and India. The present position of the continents was reached by the splitting up of the central mass and the resulting fragments drifting apart. There are many geological and geophysical arguments in support of this idea of *continental drift*.

The age of the *universe* has been calculated to be about 5,000 million years. The *earth's crust* was probably formed about 4,000 million years ago and geological history must have begun sometime after this when the first rains fell on the surface of the earth.

The crust of the earth is composed of rocks, most of which are aggregates of minerals. A *mineral* may be defined as a naturally formed inorganic substance which possesses a definite chemical composition and a definite atomic structure. Though there are hundreds of minerals which occur in nature, there are only a few which enter into the making of rocks. Such *rock-forming minerals* belong mainly to the quartz, feldspar, mica, amphibole, pyroxene, and olivine groups.

The rocks of the crust can be divided into three broad groups, (i) *Igneous rocks* such as granite and basalt, which are formed by the consolidation of molten rock material (magma), (ii) *Sedimentary rocks* such as sandstone or limestone, which are deposits formed under standing bodies of water, and (iii) *Metamorphic rocks* such as gneiss or quartzite, which are the result of modification of igneous or sedimentary rocks caused by the action of heat and/or pressure.

Igneous rocks may be *extrusive* or *intrusive*. The extrusive magma flows out from volcanic vents as *lava*. Igneous intrusions may be *minor* or *major*. Minor intrusions have two main forms—*dykes* which are steeply inclined or vertical wall-like bodies, and *sills* which are sheet-like roughly horizontal intrusions. *Major intrusions*, because of the large volume of magma, cool slowly and develop coarse textures ; such coarse-grained rocks are called *plutonic* rocks in contrast to the fine-grained *volcanic rocks* and minor intrusions.

Atmospheric agents like air and water act continually on rocks which are exposed at the surface of the earth, with the result that the rocks are chemically decomposed, or mechanically disintegrated, and the debris thus produced is transported and deposited as sediments. These processes are of great importance since they are responsible not only for the formation of *sedimentary rocks*, but also in moulding the forms of the land surface, and creating an endless variety of natural scenery.

Sediments can be classified into two broad groups. (i) *Detrital sediments* composed of particles of minerals or rocks such as pebbles, sands, or clays and (ii) *Chemical/organic sediments* represented by limestones and coals. By the consolidation of such sediments, *sedimentary rocks* are formed. Such rocks are characterised by *bedding*, each *bed* or *stratum* representing the product of a single act of sedimentation, and deposited as a nearly horizontal layer. *Bedding planes* divide the individual beds, and represent pauses in the process of deposition. *Stratification* is the name given to a succession of individual beds or strata.

Both igneous and sedimentary rocks may get buried in mobile belts and be affected by high temperatures, pressures, and chemical activity. *Metamorphism* then takes place and the rocks develop new minerals and textures. *Contact metamorphism* is produced by the heat of the igneous intrusions in the *country rocks* into which they are intrusive. *Regional metamorphism* takes place specially in mobile belts where strong stresses and high temperatures are prevalent. The textures characteristic of regionally metamorphiosed rocks are slaty, schistose, granular, and gneissose.

The surface of the earth which exposes these various types of rocks possessing different chemical and physical characteristics is continually being modified by the processes of denudation and deposition through the agencies of wind, water, ice, and gravity. This is known as *weathering*, and it involves the action of mechanical and chemical processes, often resulting in residual deposits. The movements of *ground-water* are responsible for the formation of springs and artesian basins. The chemical effects of ground-water are seen in *solution* and *deposition*. Rocks saturated by ground-water may be sufficiently lubricated to move or break up under the influence of gravity.

Water falls on the earth in the form of rain, and the *run-off* produces streams and rivers. Rivers flow because of gravity and the steeper the gradient the faster is the flow and the greater is its erosive power. Material is transported by rivers either in solution or as solid particles. When the speed of a river is lowered due to reduction in the gradient, or when the volume of water diminishes, deposition takes place of portions of the mechanical load it carries.

In polar regions or on elevated mountain tops, water solidifies into ice, and glaciers and ice-sheets are formed. The effects of erosion, transportation, and deposition by ice give rise to characteristic land-forms.

Lakes occupy basins of many different origins, and much of the mechanical load of the rivers is deposited in them. Where, for any reason, the outlet is cut off, the water becomes increasingly saline and salt lakes result.

The sea is an agent of erosion, transportation, and deposition. Currents, tides, and rivers help in coastal erosion and in forming terraces.

The most important meteorological observations for the geographer are those of temperature, pressure, winds, humidity, and precipitation, since they are the factors which cause and influence the different seasons, control the precipitation and distribution of rainfall, and give rise to vegetation characteristic of particular regions.

In the following chapters, a more detailed account will be given of the several aspects of physical geography which are summarised above. Emphasis has necessarily been laid on certain basic facts of geology such as materials and structure of the earth, and the forces which have modified the earth both internally and externally during the long period of geological time, as such facts form the foundation for understanding the mode of origin and course of development of earth features.

CHAPTER II

THE EARTH ON WHICH WE LIVE

THE EARTH AS A PLANET

THE MORE IMPORTANT MEMBERS of the solar system are the Sun, the nine planets with their satellites, and the asteroids. The Sun is believed to be the parent of all the other members. It is probable that the formation of the planets, our Earth being one of them, took place during the early stages of the development of our universe, and immediately after the creation of the stars.

The Earth occupies an intermediate place in the solar family. It is relatively close to the Sun, yet not the closest. It is a comparatively small planet, yet not the smallest. The mean distance from the Earth to the Sun is 1,486,460,000 km which is nearly three times as great as that of Mercury, but only one-thirtieth that of Neptune. The diameter of the Earth (12,742 km) is nearly twice as great as that of Mars, yet it is less than one-tenth that of Jupiter, and less than one-hundredth that of the Sun.

The density (water = 1) of the Earth is 5.52 which is only slightly greater than that of Venus (5.15), but is much greater than that of the Sun (1.4) or of Saturn (0.7).

AGE OF THE EARTH

From the earliest times men have speculated upon the origin and evolution of the earth, and stories of a creation are found in the annals of almost every race and nation. Many of these accounts now appear fantastic, but their existence indicates that the earth's history was always an endless challenge to the mind of thinking man.

The age of the earth has long been the subject of investigation by astronomers and physicists, but geologists were the first to realise that the earth must be several hundred million years old.

This conclusion was arrived at by depending mainly on the gradual development of earth features, the normal processes of sedimentation, and the evolutionary sequence indicated by fossils. In fact, in the early stages, geologists had to oppose the extreme underestimation of the age of the earth which was made by physicists.

The discovery of radioactivity opened a new chapter in the history of this investigation, and provided a powerful tool for solving the question of the ages of the different rock formations in the earth's crust, and ultimately of determining the age of the earth itself. It was found that certain elements contained in minerals are in continuous radioactive disintegration to form other elements or isotopes. This disintegration proceeds at a rate that is not only constant but is also rapid enough to be capable of being measured. It is interesting to know that many minerals in rocks contain tiny radioactive clocks of some sort which are constantly ticking away and storing up time records. These can be interpreted to give a reasonably reliable age for such minerals. Such radiometric datings are now being made all over the world, and many minerals and rocks in the earth's crust are known to be over 3,500 million years, and so, it must be at least 3,500 million years ago that the surface of the globe consolidated from a molten condition. The age of the earth itself is probably about 5,000 million years.

Shape of the Earth

Nearly 2,500 years ago, the Greek philosopher Pythagoras considered the possibility that the earth might be a sphere. The globular shape was proved beyond doubt by the circumnavigation of the world by Magellan and del Cano between 1519 and 1522 A.D. At the present time rockets go round the earth in a matter of minutes and send back pictures which provide spectacular demonstration of the curvature of the earth. The earth is not, however, perfectly spherical. The earth's rotation develops an outward centrifugal force which is maximum at the equator. There is, therefore, an equatorial bulge and a polar flattening. The polar axis is 12,713.8 km which is 43 km shorter than the equatorial diameter (12,756.8 km).

SOME NUMERICAL FACTS ABOUT THE EARTH
SIZE AND SHAPE

Equatorial semi-axis	..	6,374.4 km
Polar semi-axis	..	6,356.9 km
Mean radius	..	6,371.0 km
Equatorial circumference	..	40,077.0 km
Polar (meridian) circumference	..	40,009.0 km

AREA

Land (29.22%)	..	149 km^2
Oceans and seas (70.78%)	..	361 km^2
Total area of the earth	..	510 km^2

THICKNESS AND DENSITY

	Average thickness or radius (km)	Mean density (g/cm^3)
Oceans and seas	3.8	1.03
Continental crust (including continental shelves)	35.0	2.8
Oceanic crust (excluding continental shelves)	8.0	2.9
Mantle	2,881.0	4.53
Core	3,473.0	10.72
Whole earth	6,371.0	5.517

LAND

Greatest known height—Mt. Everest	..	8,848 m
Average height	..	840 m

OCEAN

Greatest known depth—Marianas trench	..	11,035 m
Average depth	..	3,808 m

THE SHELLS OF THE EARTH

The earth can be described as a ball of solid rock which is covered by a discontinuous sheet of water called the hydrosphere, and wrapped in an envelope of air which is known as the atmosphere.

The *atmosphere* is the layer of gases and vapours which completely surrounds the earth. It is composed mainly of a mixture of oxygen and nitrogen, with small quantities of water vapour, carbon dioxide, and inert gases such as argon. It is important since it is the medium of weather and climate, of wind, rain, and snow. The term troposphere is applied to that portion of the atmosphere next to the earth's surface in which temperature rapidly decreases with altitude, clouds form, and convection is active.

The *hydrosphere* comprises the oceans, seas, lakes, and rivers, which cover about three-quarters of the surface of the earth. Water also extends underground sometimes for hundreds of metres, filling the pore spaces and cracks in the rocks. This is called 'ground-water' and it is the main source of supply to springs and wells.

The *lithosphere* is the outer shell of the solid earth which is composed of many kinds of rocks. Soil forms its topmost layer.

Many theories of cosmogony suppose that the earth was at one time in a molten condition. During consolidation, the materials composing the earth attained a density stratification with the heaviest, composed essentially of iron and nickel, forming the deep interior *core* with an average density of 10.72; and the highest composed of silicate minerals, forming the *crust*, with an average density of 2.85. Between the crust and the core is a zone known as the *mantle*, which is made of heavy rock with an average density of 4.53. The boundary between the crust and the mantle is a surface of discontinuity which was discovered by A. Mohorovicic and is, therefore, named after him. Earthquake waves pass through the rocks above this surface with a velocity of about 7.2 km/sec, whereas in the rocks below the Mohorovicic discontinuity the velocity suddenly jumps to about 8.1 km/sec.

THE CRUST OF THE EARTH

The rocks of the crust can be divided into two contrasted groups: (i) an assemblage of light acid rocks like granite and related types, and sedimentary rocks such as sandstones and shales, with an average specific gravity of 2.7. Since these rocks are very rich in *si*lica and *al*umina, these crustal rocks are collectively known by the mnemonic term *sial*; and

(ii) an assemblage of dark and heavy basic rocks consisting mainly of basalt and related types, with a density of about 2.8 to 3.0 and also including some still heavier ultrabasic rocks, with a density up to about 3.4. These rocks contain plenty of *si*lica, iron oxides and *ma*gnesia and hence, are known by the mnemonic term *sima*.

There is practically no trace of sial in the crust which underlies the deep ocean floors. The earlier belief that the sima was a world-wide shell below the discontinuous sial layer is now found to be not quite correct. The continental crust contains an intimate mixture of sialic and basaltic rocks, so that the continents do not everywhere have a basaltic layer as their foundation, but it is generally true that basaltic and other basic rocks become increasingly abundant in the lower part of the continental crust.

MOTIONS OF THE EARTH AND THEIR EFFECTS

The earth has three principal motions. It moves with the rest of the solar system through space; it revolves around the sun once in 365.25 days in an almost circular path called its *orbit*; and it rotates on its axis once in 24 hours. The axis on which the earth rotates is an imaginary straight line passing through the centre of the earth. The points where the axis of rotation of the earth cuts the earth's surface are called the *North* and *South Poles*. The *equator* is an imaginary line drawn right round the earth exactly half way between the two poles; it divides the earth into two equal parts called *hemispheres*.

The earth's rotation gives us day and night. If the axis of rotation were perpendicular to the plane of the orbit in which the earth revolves around the sun, day and night would be of equal length at all places and at all seasons. Also, the seasons at any latitude would be almost the same throughout the year. The earth's axis, however, is not perpendicular to the plane of its orbit but is inclined by an angle of 23½ degrees. The plane in which the earth moves round the sun is called the *ecliptic*. As the earth revolves around the sun, the North and South poles always point in the same celestial direction. When it is summer in the northern hemisphere, the north half of the earth is turned toward the sun, while in the winter it is turned away from the sun. Because of the inclined position of the earth's axis, mid-latitudes have the four well defined seasons—spring, summer, autumn, and winter, while the north and south poles have six months of daylight followed by six months of darkness each year. This happens to places north of latitude 66½° N, and south of latitude 66½° S. The parallels of latitude bounding these areas of 'perpetual days' and 'perpetual nights' are known respectively as the *Arctic Circle* and *Antarctic Circle*.

The seasonal variations and the long days and nights at the poles are mainly due to the unequal amounts of heat and light received on the earth at different latitudes during the year. The earth intercepts only that part of the sunlight which falls directly upon it, and exactly one-half the earth is illuminated at any time. We may consider three positions of the earth in this connection.

On June 21st, the north end of the earth's axis—the North Pole—is inclined towards the sun. The illuminated part includes the whole of the Arctic Circle and excludes everything within the Antarctic Circle. More than half of all parallels of latitude are illuminated at one time in the northern hemisphere, and less than half in the southern hemisphere.

On March 21st and September 22nd the earth's axis is at right angles to the sun's rays, and the sun's rays reach both the poles of the earth. The length of day and night for all places on the earth are each 12 hours. These days are called the *equinoxes*, meaning 'equal nights'.

On December 22nd, the northern hemisphere is directed away from the sun; its days are therefore shorter than on June 21st. Since the southern hemisphere is now turned toward the sun, it has longer days.

From March 21st, when the midday sun is overhead at the equator, the sun seems to shift its position northwards, until on

June 21st it appears to be standing still over latitude 23½° N before it moves southwards again. In the northern hemisphere, this period of standing still is called the *summer solstice*. The latitude of 23½° N is called the *Tropic of Cancer* (tropic=turning point). Similarly, the sun appears to stand still at the *winter solstice* over latitude 23½° S on December 22nd, before it moves northwards again. The latitude of 23½° S is called the *Tropic of Capricorn*.

The part of the earth between the tropics is called the *Torrid Zone*. The part between the Tropic of Cancer and the Arctic Circle is called the *North Temperate Zone*, and that between the Tropic of Capricorn and the Antarctic Circle is called the *South Temperate Zone*. The parts north of the Arctic Circle and south of the Antarctic Circle are the *Frigid Zones*, and are distinguished as the *Arctic* and *Antarctic Zones*.

LONGITUDES AND LATITUDES

In order to indicate accurately the position of places on the surface of the earth, the globe is covered with a network of numbered reference lines consisting of two sets of circles. One set of these circles—called *meridians* or lines of *longitude*—pass through both the poles, and the centre of each is the centre of the sphere itself. They are as large as any circles drawn on the surface of the sphere can possibly be, and so the meridians are called *great circles*. The distance between them is measured in degrees of longitude. In terms of distance, one degree of longitude has the same length only at the equator (about 111 km). Elsewhere, the length decreases steadily until it becomes zero at the poles where all the meridians meet. In numbering the meridians, it is generally agreed that the count should begin from that meridian which passes through Greenwich in Great Britain. This 0° meridian is known as the *prime meridian*, from which 180° are counted eastwards and 180° westwards. Any meridian is distinguished by the angular distance between the zero point and the point, east or west of it, where that meridian cuts the equator.

Of the other set of circles, only one—the equator—is a great circle and it bisects each meridian. The other lines of latitude running east and west are *small circles* parallel to the equator, and are known as *parallels of latitude* and the distance between them is measured in degrees of latitude. The equator represents the 0° latitude. The latitudes of the northern hemisphere are north latitudes, and those of the southern hemisphere, south latitudes.

The numbering of the lines depends on referring to an arc of a circle in terms of the angle subtended by the arc at the centre of the circle. Thus, 1/360 part of the circumference of a circle is referred to as *one degree of arc* because it subtends an angle of 1° at the centre. Similarly, 1/60 of a degree of arc is called one *minute* (1'), and 1/60 of a minute, one *second* (1").

If the latitude and longitude of a place are both known, the position of that place on a terrestrial globe can be accurately fixed.

CHAPTER III

MAPS—THEIR PREPARATION AND USES

MOST COMMONLY A MAP represents in a conventional manner a part of the earth's surface somewhat as it would be seen from directly above it. One should be able to understand from a map the most important features of the region, and how those features compare with each other in size and position. However, it is impossible on a plane to represent truly the surface of a sphere. Globes furnish the only means of representing the earth accurately, but they are much too small to show the details of the earth's surface, and so maps have to be prepared. Aerial photographs are now becoming common; they give an accurate pictorial representation of the area covered.

MAP PROJECTIONS

In the making of maps, the spherical surface of the earth has to be *projected* on to a plane surface. This can be done in many different ways. Different methods of projection are used according to the purpose of the map and the area of country represented on it.

In *orthographic projection* (Fig. 1) the eye of the observer is supposed to be at an infinite distance from the earth, so that all lines drawn from it to the earth are parallel. The various points of the hemisphere are projected on a plane PL, the points A, B, C, on the globe being represented by a, b, c, on the map. The map of a hemisphere constructed by this method will only show the central portions at all correctly, the outer parts of the map being much distorted and diminished in area. This projection is fairly suitable for maps of the polar regions in which the pole forms the centre of the map; parallels of latitude then become circles, and the meridians are represented by straight lines radiating from the pole.

In the *stereographic projection* (Fig. 2) the eye is supposed to be placed at a point E on the surface of the globe and to be looking

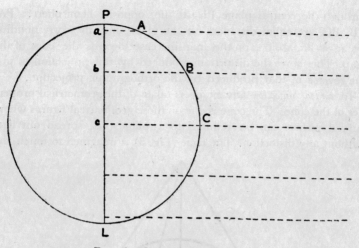

FIG. 1.   Orthographic Projection

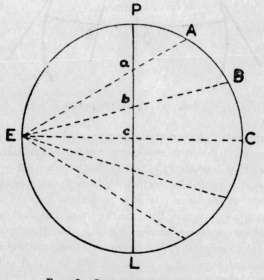

FIG. 2.   Stereographic Projection

through the central plane PL at the opposite hemisphere. PA, AB, BC, are equal distances on the globe, but the corresponding distances Pa, ab, bc, on the map increase towards the edge of the map. Therefore, the distortion produced by this projection is just the reverse of that produced by the orthographic projection.

In *conical projection* advantage is taken of the geometrical properties of the cone. The cone is one of those geometrical figures whose curved surface can be reduced to a plane (*i.e.*, spread out flat) without any distortion. The cone (Fig. 3) is imagined to touch the

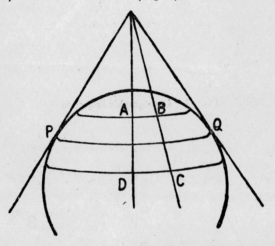

FIG. 3.   Conical Projection

surface of the earth along a particular parallel of latitude, PQ, and then that part of the surface of the globe, such as ABCD, not very distant from that latitude PQ, would be represented with great accuracy by this projection, formed by lines drawn from the centre of the sphere to the cone. In this projection lines of longitude become straight converging lines on the map, and lines of latitude become parts of concentric circles (Fig. 4). The conical projection is the one most commonly used for maps of separate countries.

The *cylindrical projection* is based on the fact that the curved surface of a cylinder, like that of a cone, can also be spread out

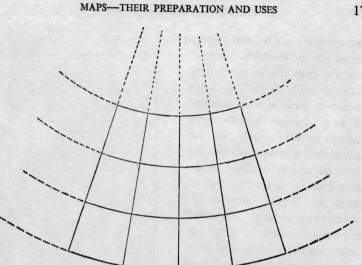

FIG. 4. Lines of Latitude and Longitude—Conical Projection

flat to form a plane. The sphere is supposed to be enclosed by a
cylinder which touches it at the equator, and the different parts
of the surface are projected on to the cylinder. There are many
methods of cylindrical projection of which the most commonly used
is that of *Mercator* (Figs. 5 and 6). In Mercator's projection, the
meridians are represented by equidistant straight lines. The parallels of latitude are also straight lines of equal length, but, to preserve the correct ratio between degrees of latitude and longitude, their
distances apart increase with the latitude. In the Mercator's net,
the exaggeration of the meridian scale at any point of the map is
exactly equal to the exaggeration of the parallel scale at that point.
Since the cylinder circumscribing the globe touches it only along
the equator, every other parallel of latitude represented as equal in
length to the equator is exaggerated. Thus at 60° N and S the parallel
scale exaggeration is exactly double and hence the meridian scale
at 60° N and S is also made double the true scale. That is, the
scale of the map, measuring east and west in latitude 60° is double
the scale at the equator, and to preserve true proportions the scale,

measuring north and south, must also be doubled. Hence, on the map the distance from latitude 60° to 61° is made twice as great as from latitude 0° to 1°, though these distances are in reality equal. By this method for small areas, the true shape of the land is approximately preserved, but its area in high latitudes is greatly exaggerated. *Mercator's projection*, though it gives no true idea of distances and areas (except near the equator) is of special importance to navigators because it gives directions accurately.

SCALE OF MAPS

The scale of a map is the *ratio* which its *linear* dimensions bear to the linear dimensions of the region represented. The scale may be expressed either as a fraction with unity as numerator, or in terms of unit of length. The scale of one inch to a mile is also a scale of $\frac{1}{63,360}$, since 63,360 inches are equal to a mile. A map on a scale of one to one-million is approximately one inch to 16 miles.

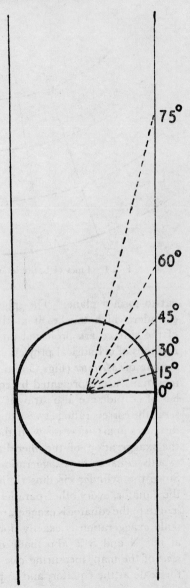

FIG. 5.   Mercator's Projection

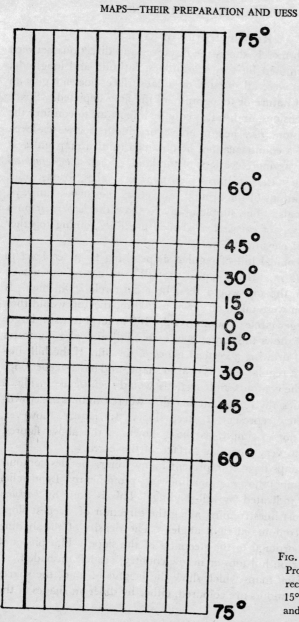

FIG. 6. Mercator's
Projection. Each
rectangle represents
15° of latitude
and longitude.

REPRESENTATION OF RELIEF

A map which merely shows the distances and directions between places as determined by two coordinates, latitude and longitude, as if such places were all situated on a flat surface, does not give an idea of the real nature or topography of the area depicted. Space is of three dimensions, and so it is equally important to consider the vertical dimension, *i.e.*, height above or depth below sea-level. A good idea of a country cannot be obtained from a map unless it represents the varying elevations of the land. Such a *topographical map* depicts the surface features such as rivers, lakes, forests, hills, and the undulations of the ground, as well as the towns, railways, roads, and canals. The simplest way to show the *land relief* on a map is by means of *contour lines*, which are lines joining together places of equal elevation.

Imagine a conical hill of regular shape rising from sea level to a height of 375 m. If the top of the hill were cut off down to a level of 300 m, the top would then be a flat circle 300m high. If another section were taken off down to 200 m, the top would then be another larger circle. Similarly, the 100 m level is a still larger circle. Fig. 7 shows the contours of such a hill and also illustrates the method of drawing a vertical *section* of the hill. If the hill, instead of being a regular cone, is oval in shape, and has a steeper slope on one side, the contours and sections would then be as in Fig. 8 which illustrates the important fact that where contours are crowded together they represent a steep slope. In nature, however, contours are not so simple as those shown in the above figures, because of the very irregular surface of the earth.

Ordinary maps have to represent many things besides contours and so they cannot show contour lines very prominently. Land-relief is sometimes indicated by hill-shading. This is done by *hachures* which are short lines running along the direction of steepest slope crossing the contours at right angles. The density of the shading is made proportional to the steepness of the slope. Flat pieces of land, whether on hill-tops or in low country, are left unshaded.

In *orographical* maps which show the heights of land, the spaces between the contours are coloured, either by different shades of the

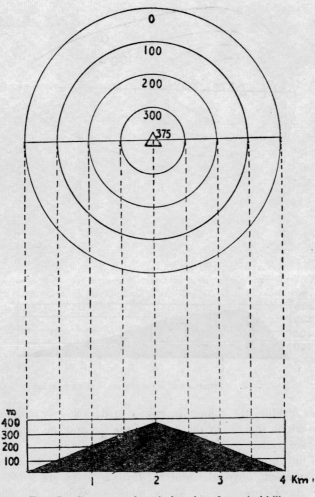

FIG. 7. Contours and vertical section of a conical hill

same colour, or by different colours. Generally shades of green are used for lowlands and shades of brown for highlands. *Bathymetric* maps are those which show the depths of the sea, usually by

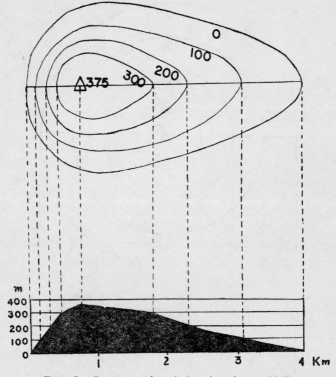

FIG. 8.   Contours and vertical section of an oval hill

shades of blue, the colour increasing in darkness with the depth.
Maps which show both the depth of the sea and the height of the
land are called *bathyorographical*.

All the above-mentioned types of maps are *physical* maps, because
they represent physical features. *Political* maps are those which
show states, towns, etc. Many maps show both physical and
political features. Maps are also drawn to represent some special
sets of facts, such as the distribution of temperature, rainfall,
vegetation, minerals etc.

CHAPTER IV

MATERIALS OF THE EARTH'S CRUST

ROCK-FORMING MINERALS

THE CRUST of the earth is composed mainly of rocks. Most rocks are made of aggregates of minerals. Though there are hundreds of minerals which occur in nature, only a few are associated in the form of rocks; they are, therefore, known as *rock-forming minerals*.

A *mineral* is a naturally formed inorganic substance which possesses a definite chemical composition and a definite atomic structure. Many minerals have a tendency to form *crystals* which are bounded by plane surfaces arranged in a regular and symmetrical manner. Some physical properties like cleavage, hardness, specific gravity, and colour, are useful in the identification of minerals.

The common minerals which make igneous rocks are *silicates* of aluminium, iron, calcium, magnesium, sodium or potassium, and silica. Seven families of these minerals make up 99% of igneous rocks. They are, in addition to *quartz* (SiO_2), the silicate minerals *feldspars* and *feldspathoids*, *micas*, *amphiboles* (hornblende), *pyroxenes* (augite), and *olivines*.

The sedimentary rocks are mainly composed of quartz and feldspar which persist from the parent igneous rock, *clay minerals*, (hydrous aluminium silicates), and the carbonates, *calcite* and *dolomite*.

The common minerals developed in metamorphic rocks include those which are present in igneous rocks. In addition, there are the silicates *serpentine*, *chlorite*, *talc*, and *garnet*, and the aluminium silicates, *andalusite*, *sillimanite*, and *kyanite*. The carbonates occur in metamorphosed limestones.

The term *rock* in the ordinary sense implies something which is hard and resistant, but in geology the term comprises all the solid material of the earth's crust, whether it is hard like granite, soft like clay, or loose like sand.

A rock is not a definite chemical compound but is composed of one or more minerals. Rocks may be divided into three great groups, *igneous* rocks, *sedimentary* rocks, and *metamorphic* rocks.

IGNEOUS ROCKS

Igneous rocks, as the word 'igneous' implies, are rocks formed through the solidification of molten material (*magma*) originating within the earth's crust. The term *plutonic* (after Pluto, the Roman god of the under-world) is applied to coarse-grained crystalline rocks like granite, which occur as major intrusions; and the term *volcanic* (after Volcanus, the Roman god of fire) to fine-grained or glassy extrusive rocks like basalt which occur as lava flows. The *hypabyssal* group includes the rocks of dykes and sills which occupy an intermediate position between the deep-seated plutonic bodies and the surficial lava flows.

Batholiths are the greatest bodies of igneous rocks known; some of them extend for about 2,000 km and have a width in places of 80 km. A batholith has a roof but has apparently no floor since the mass broadens down to unknown depths.

Among minor intrusions, two types can be distinguished. If the molten material has been guided by the bedding planes of the intruded rock, the resulting igneous body is said to be *concordant*. A *sill* is an example of such an intrusion. On the other hand, if the magma breaks across the bedding planes, the intrusion is *transgressive* or *discordant*. A *dyke* is an example of this type of intrusion. While a sill is a relatively thin tabular sheet which is approximately horizontal, a dyke is a narrow elongated wall-like intrusion which is more or less vertical.

Most lavas are heavily charged with gases, which escape as soon as the pressure is diminished by their eruption at the surface. The escape of the gases results in the formation of cavities or *vesicles*. The name *slag* or *scoria* is applied to lava in which the gas cavities are numerous. *Amygdales* are the infillings of vesicles by secondary minerals, and a rock containing them is known as an *amygdaloid*.

The important characters of igneous rocks are the *chemical composition*, the *mineral composition*, and the *texture*. The chemical composition depends on the magma from which the igneous rocks are derived. 99% of the total bulk of an igneous rock is made up of only eight elements. Of these, oxygen is the most abundant, next comes silicon, and then follow aluminium, iron, calcium, sodium, potassium, and magnesium. In terms of oxides, silica (SiO_2) is by far the most abundant, ranging from 45% to 75% of the total. Igneous rocks can be chemically classified into the following four divisions based on the silica percentage :

Acid	—	over 66% SiO_2
Intermediate	—	52 to 66% SiO_2
Basic	—	45 to 52% SiO_2
Ultrabasic	—	under 45% SiO_2.

The *mineral composition* of an igneous rock depends largely upon the chemical composition. The chief minerals present are silicates of the six common elements together with quartz if silica is in excess. The predominant minerals determine the general appearance of the rock and an idea of its composition may be obtained from its colour and density. Quartz is usually colourless and transparent, and feldspars are light in colour. Acid and intermediate rocks which are mostly made of these minerals are, therefore, usually pale in colour and relatively light in weight. The basic and ultrabasic rocks are composed of coloured and comparatively heavier minerals such as amphiboles, pyroxenes, and olivines, and so these rocks are generally dark and relatively heavy.

The *texture* of a rock is shown by the size, shape, and arrangement of the constituent minerals. *Coarse-grained* rocks are the result of slow cooling of the magma whereas *fine-grained* rocks are produced by rapid cooling. By extremely rapid cooling *glassy* rocks are formed. *Porphyritic* is the name given to the texture when crystals of two different sizes occur—the big crystals are known as *phenocrysts* and they lie in a fine-grained or glassy *groundmass*. Another characteristic texture is the *ophitic* which is common in dolerites.

A very simple classification of igneous rocks based on silica-content and grain-size is given in Table 1.

TABLE 1

Decreasing silica content———→

		Acid	Intermediate	Basic	Ultrabasic
Decreasing Grain Size ↓	Coarse-grained	Granite	Syenite Diorite	Gabbro	Peridotite Dunite
	Medium-grained	Porphyry	Porphyritic	Dolerite	
	Fine-grained or glassy	Rhyolite	Trachyte Andesite	Basalt	

SEDIMENTARY ROCKS

Sedimentary or *detrital* rocks are those formed by the deposition of the solid materials carried in suspension by transporting agents. One of the most characteristic features of sedimentary rocks is their formation in beds, layers or strata. The *bedding* or *stratification* is indicated by differences of composition, texture, hardness, or colour, disposed in approximately parallel bands. The plane of junction between different beds is a *bedding-plane*.

A single layer bounded by two bedding planes is a *bed* or *stratum*. Very fine paper-thin beds are known as *laminae*. The bedding planes are generally disposed approximately parallel to one another. Often, however, the bedding planes are inclined to the major lines of bedding An example of this type is *current bedding* (*Plate 1*), which indicates rapid changes in the direction and strength of a stream carrying sediment.

The well-known wavy pattern or *ripple mark* which is often seen on sandy beaches, may sometimes be preserved in sedimentary beds. *Sun cracks* such as can be seen on the floor of any dried-up pool, are often preserved in fine-grained sedimentary rocks.

Sedimentary rocks can be classified according to the size of their components. Rocks consisting chiefly of gravel, pebbles, or boulders are called *rudaceous*. Loose materials of this class are gravels, pebble-beds, shingle, boulder-beds, scree, talus, etc. A distinction can be made between angular and rounded fragments depending on the amount of transport the material has undergone. When consolidated, the rocks containing rounded fragments are known as *conglomerates*, and those with angular fragments as *breccias*.

Rocks consisting chiefly of sands are called *arenaceous*. When the sand grains are cemented together, the rock is a *sandstone*. A coarse sandstone with angular grains is known as a *grit*. An *arkose* is a sandstone containing grains of feldspar, and a *greywacke* is a dark coloured sandstone derived from basic igneous rocks, slates, and sandstones. *Silts* are of finer grain than sandstones, but coarser than mud or clay. *Loess* is a wind-formed calcareous silt.

Detrital deposits composed of grains whose average size is less than .01 mm are called *argillaceous* rocks. When loose and dry this material forms *dust*; with varying amounts of moisture it forms *mud* and *clay*. When argillaceous material is welded into a compact rock which is well-bedded and splits easily along the bedding planes, it is called *shale*.

Boulder clay is the most typical argillaceous rock of glacial origin, where material of clay grade is mingled with material of other grades such as pebbles, cobbles, and boulders of all sizes. Muds and clays of fluviatile origin, with silts, form the *alluvium* found along the lower courses and on the flood-plains of large rivers. *Marl* is a clay rock which contains a considerable proportion of carbonates of lime and magnesia.

Among sedimentary deposits are also grouped those of *chemical origin*. The products of rock weathering are carried away in aqueous solution and deposited by precipitation from solution or evaporation of solution. The most abundant siliceous deposits of chemical origin are *flint* and *chert*. Among carbonate deposits, *limestones* are important. By evaporation of water dripping from the roofs of limestone caves and flowing over their floors, *stalactites* and *stalagmites* are formed.

Some sedimentary deposits are due, directly or indirectly, to the vital activities of animals and plants. Among organic rocks of calcareous composition, limestones are the most important. Some of them are formed by the accumulation of organic fragments embedded in calcareous mud. Foraminifera, corals, crinoids, mollusca, and crustacea are chiefly concerned in limestone formation. Examples of such rocks are Globigerina ooze, chalk, and coral limestones. Among ferruginous deposits of organic origin mention may be made of bog iron ore. Peat, lignite, and coal are carbonaceous deposits of organic origin. All these rocks consist largely of plant debris in various stages of alteration.

METAMORPHIC ROCKS

Temperature, pressure, and chemically active fluids induce changes in igneous and sedimentary rocks. The term *thermal metamorphism* is used for all kinds of changes in which heat is the chief factor. The general metamorphism which occurs around large igneous masses is called *contact metamorphism*. The action of directed pressure leads to the mechanical breaking down of rocks (cataclasis). Such metamorphism which results through the dominant action of stress is called *cataclastic metamorphism*. The combination of directed pressure and heat is very powerful in producing metamorphism because it leads to more or less complete recrystallisation of rocks and the production of new structures. This kind of metamorphism is known as *dynamic* or *dynamothermal metamorphism*.

The combination of uniform pressure and heat dominates conditions of metamorphism at depths where directed pressure ceases because of the increasing plasticity of the rocks. Mineral transformations take place but new structures are not developed. *Plutonic metamorphism* is a suitable name for changes under such conditions. Evenly granular rocks like *granulites* are formed.

In some cases the metamorphic agencies may operate only very locally causing *local metamorphism*; in other cases they may bring about great changes over extensive areas causing *regional metamorphism*.

Pressure causes the arrangement of the mineral constituents of a metamorphic rock with their long axes more or less parallel, thus causing the rock to have a parallel structure or *foliation*. Well-developed foliation causes *rock cleavage*, that is, a tendency for the rock to split in layers parallel to the foliation. Foliation which is well developed in a very fine-grained but not obviously crystalline rock is called *slaty cleavage*. A good example is afforded by the rock *slate*.

A highly crystalline rock with good cleavage and platy minerals plainly visible in it is called a *schist*. A highly crystalline rock with a crudely developed foliation is a *gneiss*.

Schists and gneisses can be developed by the metamorphism of sedimentary rocks also. Thus shales can give rise to *mica*-or *hornblende-schist* and *gneiss*. Quartz schist is foliated impure sand-stone often containing mica. Many slates are foliated shales with highly developed slaty cleavage but with very little crystallisation.

Among the non-foliated metamorphosed sedimentary rocks are *quartzite*, a hard massive rock derived from fairly pure quartz-sandstone, and *marble* derived from limestone.

CHAPTER V

MOVEMENTS OF THE EARTH'S CRUST

IRREGULARITIES OF THE EARTH'S SURFACE

NEWTON'S LAW OF GRAVITATION afforded an explanation for the spherical shape of the earth, for, according to this law, all the particles of the earth are pulled towards the centre of gravity and the spherical shape would be the natural result. Newton also gave an explanation for the earth not being exactly spherical. Along with the gravitational pull towards the centre, there was also an outward centrifugal force caused by the earth's rotation which reached its maximum at the equator, which would result in an equatorial bulge and a polar flattening. So, if the surface of the earth were everywhere at sea-level the shape of the earth would be an elipsoid of rotation (oblate spheroid) with a polar axis which is slightly (43 km) shorter than the equatorial diameter. But again, neither is the earth a perfectly oblate spheroid.

The reason for the earth not being exactly a spheroid is that the rocks of the earth's crust do not have the same density. In places, therefore, where the gravity is low, that is, wherever light sialic rocks form the crust, there would be bulges. Such regions are the continents. In those places, however, where the crust is composed of heavy simatic rocks and the gravity is consequently high, there would be depressions. Such places are the ocean basins. It is because of these differences of density and thickness in the rocks of the crust that continents, mountains, and oceanic basins occur as irregularities on the surface of the spheroid.

ISOSTASY

In 1889 Dutton, an American geologist, proposed the term *isostasy* (from a Greek word meaning 'equipoise') for the gravitational equilibrium which determines the heights of continents and the depths of the ocean floors in conformity with the densities of the rocks underlying them. According to this concept, blocks of the earth's crust because of variations in densities would rise to different levels and appear on the surface as mountains, plateaus, plains, or ocean basins.

During a survey of the Indo-Gangetic plain about a hundred years ago by the Survey of India, the difference in latitude between Kalianpur and Kaliana (600 km due north) was determined astronomically as well as by direct triangulation on the ground. The two values differed by 5.23 seconds of arc, corresponding to a distance in the ground of 168 m. This difference was considered to be due to the attraction exerted on the plumb line by the enormous rock mass composing the Himalayas. A few years later, Archdeacon Pratt made an estimate of the mass of the mountains, and calculated what the deflections of the plumb line towards the mountains should be at the two places Kalianpur and Kaliana. The calculated difference was 15.885″ which was more than three times the observed deflection, 5.23″. The explanation for this anomaly is that the density of the rocks must be comparatively low down to considerable depths.

Based on the above observations, as well as on exploration of the crust by earthquake waves, it is inferred that mountain ranges have "roots" going down to depths of 50 or 60 km, which are largely composed of light sialic rocks. Below the plains near sea-level, the thickness of the sial is only about 30 km or less. There is no sial beneath the deeper parts of the oceans.

The great features of the crust such as continents, mountains, plateaus, and ocean basins, are in isostatic equilibrium. This equilibrium is, however, upset now and then by the results of geological action. If, for example, great volumes of eroded material are washed down from a mountain range and deposited in the sea, the crustal column under the mountains becomes lighter, and the column under the sea becomes heavier. In order to restore the equilibrium, slow vertical movements take place which raise or lower the affected parts of the crust. Also, slow lateral movements of dense material beneath the sial adjust the deeper layers. The workings of isostasy, therefore, are sometimes responsible for earth-movements, and may explain such phenomena as the uplift of marine sediments to high levels.

CONTINENTAL DRIFT

We have already seen that at the present time the sialic material which forms the continents is not spread in an even layer but is grouped in relatively small tabular blocks covering only about one-third of the earth's surface. The exact reason for this distribution is not clear. It is generally believed that the sialic layer was once continuous, and that the concentration in the continents took place as a result of the folding in mobile belts, or due to being massed together by the drag of slow convection currents in the mantle. On the other hand, there may have been only a single continental mass (*Pangaea* of Wegener), or two polar continents, or perhaps four corresponding to the points of a tetrahedron.

There has been considerable controversy regarding the *permanence* of continents and oceans, *i.e.*, whether the continental blocks and main ocean basins have remained in the same places throughout geological history. This would imply that if the sial had once been continuous, the land-masses have disappeared by sinking under the oceans. This is most unlikely since it is now known that the main ocean basins are floored almost directly by sima and contain practically no sialic continental material. There is no evidence also that the floors of these ocean basins have at any time been uplifted to form new continents.

According to the widely accepted theory of *continental drift*, there was a great Southern Continent comprising South America, Africa, India, Australia, and Antarctica, to which the collective name *Gondwanaland* has been applied. Soon after the close of Palaeozoic times, Gondwanaland began to break up into gigantic crustal blocks which glided slowly over the substratum of sima and mantle, and changed both their relative situations as well as their positions with reference to the north and south poles.

There are many geological and geophysical arguments in support of continental drift. A spectacular evidence is the remarkable fit, like a jig-saw puzzle, of the Atlantic coast-

PLATE 1—**Current bedding in sandstones, Raniganj Coalfield.** (See Page 26)

PLATE 2—**Pillow lava, Dharwar Group. Maradihalli, Mysore State.** (See page 38) (*Photo*—C.S. Pichamuthu).

PLATE 4—**View of Mount Everest, Himalayas.** (See Page 43) (*Photo*—A.M. Heron).

lines of South America and Africa. Equally convincing is the similarity in the geological history and structure of these lands west and east of the Atlantic Ocean. Another compelling evidence is that the sediments deposited during the Permo-Carboniferous glaciation are found in parts of South Africa, Australia, Antarctica, and India. At the present period, these continents are scattered over a great extent of the earth's surface, and many of them lie in tropical latitudes where there is no possibility of the existence of conditions necessary for the formation of ice. It is most likely that when glaciation set in, these continents were grouped together near the south pole (Fig. 9).

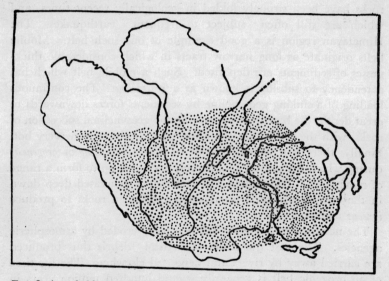

Fig. 9. A probable assembly of Gondwanaland during the Carboniferous period. The dotted area shows the distribution of glaciation (after Holmes)

Orogeny and Epeirogeny

The term *diastrophism* includes all movements of the earth's crust. They may be divided into sudden movements such as earthquakes, and slow movements. Slow but relatively large movements are of two types : *orogenic*, where a long and narrow belt is subjected to a force of compression causing the rock formations to be folded and raised up to form a mountain range; and *epeirogenic*, where there is either elevation or subsidence of a large or a small part of the earth's crust without any considerable compression or folding of the rocks, whose former attitude may not be changed, or may be gently upwarped or downwarped, or more or less tilted. Plateaus result from epeirogenic movements of uplift. In general, diastrophic forces which have uplifted lands have predominated over forces which have lowered them.

We can recognise at the present time *mobile belts* in which the rocks have been strongly folded in geologically recent times, and which are still often subject to frequent earthquakes. The Himalayan region is a good example of one such belt. Mobile belts originate as long narrow tracts in which considerable thicknesses of sediments are deposited. Such a mobile belt which has a tendency to subside is known as a *geosyncline*. The continuous loading of a sinking geosyncline by sediments forces downwards to great depths the basement underlying the geosynclinal succession of rocks, with the result that the lower parts begin to grow very hot. Finally, there is a violent episode of *mountain-building* or *orogenesis* during which the narrow mobile belt is thrown up to form a range of mountains. The molten material that is generated deep down in the crust is squeezed up through the folded rocks to produce *igneous intrusions*.

The newly-formed *orogenic belt* is rapidly eroded by atmospheric agencies. The vast quantities of detrital debris thus produced are carried away by rivers and deposited elsewhere. The life-time of an orogenic belt is generally several hundred million years in length.

Epeirogenic movements affect considerable parts of a continent or sea-floor and cause elevation or subsidence without notable compression or folding, though there may be gentle warping of the crust. Fracturing or faulting of the rock masses often accompany epeirogenic disturbances.

In order to evaluate the magnitude of the upward or downward

movement of land, there should be a *datum* line.   The surface of the
sea is a very satisfactory datum since it maintains, within narrow
limits, an average tidal level.   All heights mentioned on maps are
elevations above the mean sea level.   The records of earth history
contain many instances of minor changes of level which have taken
place between land and sea.

ELEVATION OF LAND

Raised beaches, elevated wave-cut terraces, sea caves and
fossiliferous beds above sea level are evidences of uplift. One of
the reasons for believing that the Deccan was uplifted is that the
Nummulitic limestones rest unconformably on the basaltic lavas
near Surat well above sea level.

SUBSIDENCE OF LAND

Submerged forests and valleys, as well as buildings, are evidences
of subsidence.

A part of the Rann of Kutch was submerged as the result of an
earthquake in 1819.

The Andamans and Nicobars have been isolated from the
Arakan coast by submergence.

On the east side of Bombay Island, trees have been found
imbedded in mud about 4 m below low-water mark. A similar
submerged forest has also been noticed on the Tirunelveli coast in
Madras State.

CHAPTER VI

VOLCANOES AND EARTHQUAKES

IN CHAPTER IV *igneous rocks* have been defined as those produced by the solidification of molten rock-material or *magma*. Igneous rocks represent material brought up from deep within the earth. The fine-grained or glassy rocks which occur as lava flows were referred to as *volcanic rocks*. The igneous activity which is revealed by volcanic action can be studied at the earth's surface in several places, whereas igneous processes which operate far below the surface can only be investigated by geophysical or other allied techniques.

VOLCANIC ACTIVITY AND ITS PRODUCTS

A *volcano* is essentially a vent or fissure in the earth's crust, communicating with the earth's interior, from which flows of molten rock material (*lava*), fountains of red-hot spray, or explosive bursts of gases and volcanic 'ashes' are erupted at the surface. A great explosive volcanic action is probably the most spectacular and most terrifying of all natural phenomena. From the geological standpoint, however, volcanoes are of much less importance than the enormous internal forces which cause the rocks of the earth's crust to be faulted and folded, and large parts of continents to be upheaved or depressed.

The accumulation of the erupted material around the vent results in the formation of a *cone*, with a funnel-shaped *crater* at the top from which the hot rock materials and gases are thrown out. Volcanoes with the familiar cone-and-crater structure are said to be of the *central* type because the activity is centralised about a pipe-like conduit. Very large craters, often called *calderas*, are formed either by violent explosions which blow off the tops of great cones, or by subsidence of the mountain tops.

In contrast to the central type, a volcano sometimes erupts from a *fissure*. Such eruptions are not very explosive, and are also characterised by the absence of large amounts of gases and fragmental materials. The Deccan Trap flows of India are believed to have issued from great fissures.

A few volcanoes remain more or less continually in eruption for long periods but intermittent activity is more common. Some volcanoes continue to be *dormant* (from the Latin word *dormir* meaning 'to sleep') with long intervals of repose during which all external signs of activity cease. Before a volcano becomes *extinct*, it passes through a waning stage during which steam and other hot gases and vapours are exhaled. These are known as fumaroles or *solfataras*.

There are about 500 volcanoes in the world that can be classed as *active* at the present time. There are no volcanoes in the Himalayan region or in the Indian peninsula. Barren Island in the Bay of Bengal, to the east of the Andaman Islands, is now a dormant volcano. There is only a truncated remnant of a once much larger caldera. It is an outer amphitheatre more than 3 km in diameter which surrounds an inner symmetrical cone whose crater is about 350 m above the level of the sea, but the base of the cone lies some thousands of metres below the surface of the sea. It has remained dormant since its eruption early in the nineteenth century, but later passed into a mild solfataric stage as evidenced by the sublimations of sulphur on the walls of the crater. The other volcanic island in Indian territory is Narcondam, about 150 km northeast of Barren Island; this is probably extinct. Its crater wall has been completely destroyed.

There is a strikingly close agreement between volcanic and earthquake zones of the earth which indicates that there is a definite relationship between these two great groups of phenomena. The location of volcanoes on the steep continental borders near great ocean deeps and in or near youthful mountains correlates them definitely with zones of weakness in the earth's crust.

Steam is the commonest of volcanic gases emitted by a volcano. It is probable that they are derived mainly from superficial sources such as crater lakes, ground-water, and the sea. Besides steam, the other gases consist of carbon dioxide, nitrogen and sulphur dioxide, and minor quantities of hydrogen, carbon monoxide, sulphur, and chlorine.

The molten materials which issue from out of volcanoes as well as the rocks which result from their cooling, are called *lavas*. The source is the molten rock material of the earth's interior known as *magma*. The white-hot lava issuing from the crater changes to a dull-red glow as it flows from the mountain side. As it gradually cools, the lava becomes more viscous, and minerals start crystallising till the whole mass becomes solid lava. Basaltic lavas are very mobile and flow freely for long distances. The Deccan Traps which are composed of such lavas, cover to-day an area of 5,00,000 km², but their present distribution is no measure of their past extension because denudation has been at work for thousands of years, cutting through the basalts and detaching a number of outliers which are separated from the main area by great distances. These outliers indicate that the original extent of the formation must have been at least 14,00,000 km². Acid lavas (silica-rich) on the other hand, are very viscous and do not travel far.

When lava flows over the sea-floor or is otherwise in contact with water, it consolidates with a structure like that of a jumbled heap of cushions, and is then described as *pillow lava*. Excellent examples of pillow lavas of Precambrian age are to be seen in parts of Mysore State (*Plate 2*).

Columnar structure is sometimes developed in fine-grained plateau basalts of uniform texture. Very good columnar basalts are seen in the Deccan Traps near Bombay (*Plate 3*).

The explosive action of a volcano throws into the air highly heated materials which fall to the ground as solid fragments which may vary in size from very small dust particles to masses weighing tonnes. Such fragmental materials are known as *pyroclasts*. The pyroclastic materials are derived from the walls of the pipe of the volcano, from the consolidated lava which plugs the pipe, and from the upper part of the column of magma which fills the pipe.

Volcanic bombs result from masses of molten material which are sent whirling through the air and which consolidate with somewhat rounded forms. *Volcanic cinders* are fragmental materials which range in size from about 2 cm to dust particles. Larger cinders are called *lapilli* and smaller ones *ashes*. These are not, however, products of combustion. *Volcanic dust* is the most finely divided material ejected from volcanoes. They are often thrown many kilometres into the air and remain suspended for long periods and carried by atmospheric currents for hundreds or even thousands of kilometres. Layers of volcanic dust and ashes are often compacted into a rock called *tuff*.

EARTHQUAKES — CAUSES AND EFFECTS

Earthquakes are among the most terrifying of all natural phenomena because of the terrible loss of life and property which results from them. An *earthquake* is a shaking or trembling of the earth, caused by the sudden movement of a part of the earth's crust. The chief cause of earthquake shocks is the sudden slipping of rock formations along faults. Some quakes originate at depths as great as several hundred kilometres where the temperature and pressure conditions are very high. The actual shifting of the land at the time of an earthquake occurs only in a narrow zone on either side of the fault line. In such a case, the main zone of shock and consequent destruction is linear because the vibrations originate in the line of fracture. A sudden slipping of even five to fifteen metres along a line of fracture 80 to several hundred kilometres long can cause a very severe earthquake.

Another cause of earthquake is volcanic activity, but this is much less important. Such earthquakes are probably caused by the sudden subterranean yielding of the earth's crust under the influence either of increasing pressure of volcanic gases or the movement of molten rocks struggling to escape. Earthquakes of volcanic origin are generally less severe and more limited in extent than those caused by fracturing of the earth's crust.

Minor causes of earthquakes are landslides, submarine slides, and collapse of cavern roofs.

Earthquakes are so common that it may be said that the surface of the earth is at no time entirely free from earthquake vibrations.

A great many of these shocks are slight; only occasionally are the shocks very severe.

The vibrations of earthquakes which can be felt by human beings last from a few seconds to several minutes. Generally, the greater the intensity of the shock, the longer they last. The average duration of shocks of sufficient intensity to produce much damage is perhaps from one to two minutes.

It must be understood that the earth instead of being an excessively rigid body is really more or less elastic. A sudden impulse, therefore, makes a part of the earth to vibrate. The vibrations travel out in wave-like form into the earth in all directions from the source of the shock. Earthquake waves travel ordinarily at the rate of about 5 to 8 km per second through the outer part of the crust but travel faster with depth.

Earthquake waves are of three types. These are: (1) Primary or P waves, also called longitudinal waves or waves of compression, which travel outward in straight lines in all directions from the focus of the shock. They are the fastest of all earthquake waves having an average velocity of 5.3 km a second and a maximum of nearly double that rate. In the P waves, the particles move backward and forward in the direction along which they are transmitted.

(2) Secondary, S or shear waves, also called transverse waves, because the particles vibrate at right angles to the direction of propagation. They closely follow the P waves. The velocity of the S wave is about one-half that of the P wave, but the S wave is more destructive. On reaching the surface of the earth these waves cause the rocking motion of the earthquake.

(3) After the P or S waves reach the surface of the earth, a surface wave L may be formed which travels around along or near the surface portion of the earth with a lower velocity than the other two. L waves are also very destructive. In a great earthquake, the L waves may throw the ground into a series of actual undulations which may rise in long, low, rapidly moving waves that cause trees and tall structures to sway violently.

At distant points on the earth the different kinds of earthquake waves can be more or less separately recorded by a very sensitive instrument called a *seismograph*.

The secondary transverse waves do not pass through the earth below a depth of about 2,900 km. This clearly shows that the interior of the earth is of a different nature than the outer portion. Since transverse waves pass through solids only, the inner core of the earth may possibly have properties similar to that of liquids.

The actual effects of earthquakes on topography are comparatively small. The vibrations often set off landslides especially in hilly regions; loose mantle-rock is cracked open or caused to slump; small circular openings like miniature volcanic craters are formed in soil and unconsolidated rock; irregular cracks may develop parallel with or transverse to the faults that caused the earthquake; the disturbance of the earth's crust may cause old springs to stop flowing or new springs to develop.

Earthquakes sometimes take place under the ocean and produce sea-waves of great size and velocity which are known as *tsunamis*. Tsunamis may be from 80 to 300 km from crest to crest, and up to 15 m high where they originate. They travel at a speed of hundreds of kilometres per hour, and often cause considerable damage to wharves, shipping, and houses.

EARTHQUAKES IN INDIA

Peninsular India is fairly free from earthquakes, whereas the extra-Peninsular region is subject to frequent shocks, often of great severity. This is because the extra-Peninsular region is a zone of the Himalayas; in fact, the region has not yet attained stability, and slight movements are still taking place. Apart from displacements occurring along the Himalayan boundary faults or thrusts, the presence of a strained zone of crumpled and fractured rocks below the Indo-Gangetic alluvium must be considered as a source of earthquakes. The earthquake zone of India falls within the great earthquake belt which traverses the earth from east to west.

One of the most violent earthquakes in India was that which occurred in Assam in 1897. In less than one minute, Shillong with the surrounding country of 3,90,000 km^2 was laid waste, because all communications were destroyed, the plains affected by numerous gaping fissures from which issued fountains of water, and the hill-sides scarred by gigantic landslides.

The Kangra earthquake of 1905 was even more violent and destructive as it killed about 20,000 people. The shock was felt over the whole of India north of the Tapti valley. The main shock was sudden but hundreds of after-shocks of moderate intensity were felt for several months. Slight alterations took place in the level of some places, *e.g.*, Dehra Dun, and the Siwalik Hills showed a rise of about 35 cm relatively to Mussoorie.

The Bihar earthquake of 1934 was also one of great intensity. Within a few minutes, the cities of Monghyr and Bhatgaon (Nepal) were in ruins, and buildings were considerably damaged in towns as far apart as Kathmandu, Patna, and Darjeeling. Numerous fissures opened on either side of the Ganga from which water and sand were thrown up. Twelve thousand persons lost their lives.

CHAPTER VII

MOUNTAINS AND THEIR FORMATION

MOUNTAINS ARE THE SPECTACULAR products of deforming forces acting on the earth's crust. They are called *mountains* because their peaks stand from a few hundred to several thousand metres above the surrounding terrain. A mountain may be defined as a conspicuous high land with a small summit area. Low mountains are known as *hills*, but the terms are entirely relative. A mountain *peak* is an isolated more or less cone-shaped feature. Mount Everest is a good example (*Plate 4*). A mountain *ridge* is relatively long and narrow. A mountain *range* is a group of ridges and peaks, often with more or less parallel arrangement, which are closely associated in age and origin. The Himalayas is an illustration of this type. A mountain *system* consists of many ranges belonging to a common region of elevation and generally either parallel or in consecutive lines. A mountain *chain* consists of two or more systems or ranges which are more or less independent in age and origin, but occurring in a long narrow band.

ORIGIN OF MOUNTAINS

Most of the great mountain ranges and systems of the earth are diastrophic in origin. The Himalayan range furnishes an outstanding example of this mode of formation. A structural study of such a range shows the action of tremendous earth movements, and that faults, broad upwarps, and folds have contributed to the mountain structures.

All great folded ranges stand on the sites of great downwarps which are known as *geosynclines*. During the earth's history, geosynclines have at various times and at various places been the sites of accumulation of very extensive piles of strata reaching total thicknesses of many thousands of metres. Such sediment-filled geosynclinal basins have usually been subjected to enormous lateral pressure, with the result that the sedimentary formations have been strongly folded and raised into mountain ranges. The folds are now exposed as a result of removal of overlying material by subsequent erosion. The main axes of the folds are generally parallel to the trend of a folded range because the compressive force was exerted at right angles to the trend of the range. Such an elongated zone of the earth's crust which began as a geosyncline is known as an *orogenic belt*.

Mountains formed primarily by *faults* are found in many parts of the earth. Blocks of land may be lifted up along two roughly parallel fault planes, giving rise to a *horst*. Sometimes there is an upthrust on one side with warping or tilting on the other. The movement in all these cases is vertical or near vertical.

In many mountains *folding* of the rocks is the dominant structure. Faults almost invariably occur in strongly folded ranges, and igneous intrusions and extrusions usually accompany or follow the uplift of the mountains. The folding may be simple elongated domes, a series of anticlines and synclines, or complicated overfolds, which may result in the *nappe structure*.

The *volcanic* mountains are formed of material which emanate from the craters. Such cones or domes occur as independent chains and groups, the heights varying from low domes to great elevations.

Plateaus and high plains when much eroded can result in *residual* mountains. Canyons first develop, and as erosion advances the remnants left between stream tributaries form mountains. Sometimes the parent plateau out of which the mountains were carved has nearly disappeared, but its former surface can be reconstructed from the accordant summits of the present mountains.

MOUNTAINS OF INDIA

India has several mountain ranges, chief among them being the Himalayas, the Vindhya, the Aravalli, the Satpura, the Western Ghats, and the Eastern Ghats.

The Himalayas (from the Sanskrit words *hima*=snow+*alaya* =abode meaning 'abode of snow') constitute the highest mountain system of the world. They extend for a distance of 2,500 km, are 150 to 400 km broad, and cover about 5,00,000 km². They are typically tectonic in origin, having been uplifted during the Tertiary times from the bed of the great mediterranean sea, the Tethys. The Himalayas took probably several million years to attain their present height. These uplift movements have not yet ceased for this region is still unstable and susceptible to earthquakes. During the slow process of mountain formation by the folding and upheaval of the rock beds, the old rivers kept very much to their own channels and hence, are seen to cut across these mighty ranges. For example, the west-flowing river Sutlej has cut across a 6,000 m high range and runs through a steep-sided valley.

The Himalayan chain has an arcuate trend with the convex side facing the Indo-Gangetic plain. The southern boundary is clearly demarcated by the 300 m contour line in the west and the 150 m contour line in the east. From the foot-hills the Himalayas rise rapidly northwards to over 8,000 m within a short distance. The heights are covered with perpetual snow which feeds the valley glaciers, but the greater part of the Himalayas lies below the snow-line and is dissected by fluvial erosion.

The Himalayan mountains can be divided into three parallel or longitudinal zones, each with definite orographical features— the Great Himalaya (Himadri) in the north, the Lesser Himalaya (Himachal) in the middle, and the outer Himalaya (Siwalik) in the south.

The Great Himalaya or *the Himadri* is a majestic range of mountains which rises above the limit of perpetual snow. The average elevation extends to 6,000 m, and some of the highest peaks are situated in this range — Mount Everest (8,848 m), (*Plate 4*), K² (8,611 m), Kanchenjunga (8,598 m), Dhaulagiri (8,172 m), Nanga Parbat (8,126 m), Gesherbrum (8,035 m), Gosainthan (8,013 m), Nanda Devi (7,817 m), and others. This great mountain arc terminates at both its western and eastern ends where there are sharp syntaxial bends. The northern slopes of the Great Himalayan range descends gradually on to some prominent river valleys which run parallel for long distances.

The Lesser Himalaya or *the Himachal* is a massive mountainous tract, 75 km wide. The mountains and valleys are disposed in all directions, the mountains rising to 5,000 m, and the valleys touching 1,000 m. The summits are somewhat about the same elevation which suggests that this mountain belt is a highly dissected plateau.

The Outer Himalaya or *the Siwalik* forms the foot-hills and lies between the Lesser Himalaya and the plains. Their width varies from 10 to 50 km, and the average elevation is 600 m. They are composed mainly of Upper Tertiary sedimentary river deposits. They are folded and faulted by earth movements which mark the latest phase of the Himalayan uplift. The ranges descend northwards into flat valleys called *duns* which are intensively cultivated and densely populated.

The *Aravalli* mountains cross Rajasthan from southwest to northeast dividing the arid semi-desert of the Bikaner, Jodhpur, and Jaisalmer area on the west from the more fertile region of Udaipur and Jaipur on the east. They are the remnants of former mountain ranges of tectonic origin. Guru Sikhar (1,722 m) on the Abu hills is the highest peak of the Aravalli.

The *Vindhya* range stretches across nearly the whole width of Peninsular India, a distance of nearly 1,050 km with an average elevation of 300 m. It forms an important watershed, and along with the Satpura range, constitutes the northern boundary of the Deccan.

The *Satpura* range lies south of the Vindhya and runs more or less parallel to it. Several of its peaks are over 1,000 m high, the highest being Dhupgarh (1,350 m) near Pachmarhi hill station. The Satpuras consist of a number of parallel ranges which enclose between them extensive flat-topped lava plateaus. The Satpuras broaden considerably in the central part and have a radial drainage; this part is bordered on the north by the Mahadeo hills, and on the south by the Gawilgarh hills.

The *Western Ghats* (*Sahyadri*) with an average height of 1,200 m runs almost parallel to the coast for about 1,600 km along the western border of the Deccan from the mouth of the Tapti river to Cape Comorin. Up to the 16° N latitude from the Tapti, the ranges are composed of horizontal sheets of basaltic lava flows which exhibit typical trap features. The Ghats rise almost perpendicularly from the coastal plain up to a height of 1,000 m in some places. The steep face looks like an ancient sea-cliff, but it is probably a fault scarp the western part of which has drifted away westwards. This special feature accounts for the fact that all the important rivers of Peninsular India, except the Narmada and the Tapti, flow eastwards into the Bay of Bengal, though their sources are on the crest of the Ghats which is only 50 to 80 km from the Arabian Sea. The crest line runs in broad curves forming two-re-entrants at Trimbak and Tamhini, carved respectively by the headwaters of the Godavari and Bhima rivers. Kalsubai (1,646 m), Salher (1,567 m), and Mahabaleshwar (1,438 m), are among the highest peaks in this part of the Western Ghats.

From 16° N. latitude to the Nilgiri mountain, granite and gneiss take the place of Deccan Trap. In this section, the Ghats run close to the coast until they join the Nilgiri mountain near Gudalur.

The Palghat Gap trending east-west lies across the Ghats. The gap is 24 km wide at its narrowest part and lies at an elevation of 144 m, while the bordering hills rise to heights of 1,500 m to 2,000 m. This gap is probably a rift valley caused by subsidence between two parallel faults.

The Western Ghats continue south of the Palghat Gap. Anai Mudi (2,695 m) is a nodal point from which three ranges radiate— the Anaimalai in the north, the Palni Hills in the northeast, and the Cardamon Hills (Elamalai) in the south.

The Eastern Ghats :- The northern section of the Eastern Ghats lies in Orissa State and Andhra Pradesh, with an average width of 200 km in the north and 100 km in the south. Mahendragiri (1,501 m) in Orissa is a conspicuous peak lying above the coastal plain. The general trend of the ranges is northeast to southwest. The prevailing rock type is khondalite.

In the Deccan, the Eastern Ghats do not form a continuous range except in the Cuddapah and Kurnool districts of Andhra Pradesh. Between the Pennar and Krishna rivers, there are

parallel ranges and valleys of the Eastern Ghats which trend north-
south. The most prominent of these ranges is the Nallamala
which runs parallel to the Coromandel coast. The Cauvery cuts
the range transversely near Sivasamudram in Mysore State, and
later leaps over the Hogenakal falls. Near the southern end of the
Ghats, the Biligirirangan Hills (highest peak, 1,750 m) forms a
well-defined range.

To the east of the Eastern Ghats, there are two other groups of
hills : the southern group dominated by the Shevaroy Hills, and the
northern by the Javadi hills.

The *Nilgiri* or *Blue Mountain* is the meeting ground of the Western
Ghats and the Eastern Ghats. The Nilgiri mountain rises abruptly
from the plains in a stupendous precipice which is probably a fault
scarp. The general trend of the Nilgiri is northeast—southwest,
which corresponds to the trend of the Eastern Ghats. Two of
the highest peaks are Dodda Betta (2,637 m) and Makurti (2,554
m). The south-western part of the mountain known as Kunda,
is traversed by bold ranges and intersected by deep valleys. The
surface of the rest of the Nilgiri is extremely undulating with rounded grassy hills and broad forest-clad valleys.

PLATE 3—**Columnar structure in Deccan Traps, near Bombay.** (See Page 38)

PLATE 5—**Steeply dipping beds of quartzite, Rajasthan.** (See Page 56)

CHAPTER VIII

PLAINS AND PLATEAUS

PLAINS AND THEIR ORIGIN

PLAINS are the relatively low lands of the earth. Their surface irregularities are comparatively small. They may be very flat or moderately rolling. They are formed both by internal earth forces, and by external processes of aggradation or degradation. Some are of small size, but there are also very large plains.

Plains are of great importance in man's physical environment because practically all the large cities of the world are situated on plains and the great majority of the peoples of the earth live on plains. This is because most of the largest and richest agricultural regions of the world are on plains; the relatively low relief of plains makes communications and transportation facilities easier to develop than on mountains or plateaus.

Plains of great extent have been formed by the uplift of a marginal sea bottom, or by the withdrawal of the sea. They occur on continental borders only slightly above sea level and are known as *coastal plains*. *Interior plains* are those which are situated in the interior of a continent. If parts of continents have been raised by diastrophism without much dislocation of the rocks so that the surface of the land still maintains its low relief, they are known as *high plains*.

Peneplains represent large land areas of low relief that have been reduced nearly to base level by the combined action of weathering and streams. The surfaces of peneplains are not flat but gently rolling, with low hills standing as island-like erosion remnants above the general surface of the land. There are few large peneplains at base level today, but there are many *uplifted* peneplains some of which were originally true plains.

Flood-plains and *delta plains* are closely associated in origin and in present geographical position. Distributary streams, swamps, ox-bow lakes, and abandoned channels are common in such plains. The soils are extremely fertile, but flood dangers are great.

Coastal plains are somewhat temporary features that may be submerged or elevated by local diastrophism, but the great interior plains are likely to endure for a very long time with only minor changes of their surfaces. Plains now existing near base level are not subject to rapid erosion by streams. High or steeply inclined plains can be profoundly affected by erosion and reach, like mountains and plateaus, maximum ruggedness during the mature stages of their erosional history.

PLAINS OF INDIA

The plains of India are of great importance from the human point of view, as they have been centres of ancient cultures. Almost all the different types of plains are found in India.

Alluvial plains. An outstanding example is the Indo-Gangetic plain which lies in front of the Himalayas, stretching from the arid and semi-arid plains of Rajasthan in the west to the Ganga delta in the east. The northern boundary of this plain is well-defined, but the southern boundary is a wavy irregular line along the northern edge of Peninsular India. The Indo-Gangetic plain is a 'fore-deep' formed either by downwarp or as a rift-valley. It is at present an alluvium-filled trough. The total area of the plain is 6,52,000 km^2, of which one-third lies in the arid region of western Rajasthan. The thickness of the alluvium is maximum in the Ganga plains, and minimum in the western plains. The surface of this plain is at tide level near the mouth of the Ganga but in the Punjab it is over 200 m above sea level. The Indus and the Ganga have a number of large tributaries which flow parallel for long distances.

The drier parts of the plain in the Punjab extend southwards and gradually merge with the arid plain of Rajasthan which is known as the Thar Desert. Though this region is a part of the Indo-Gangetic alluvial plain, it is different in that the action of wind is predominant over that of flowing surface water. Most of this arid plain was under the sea from the Permo-Carboniferous period until it was uplifted during the Pleistocene. The existence of several dry beds of rivers indicates that the region was once fertile. At present, the Luni (or Salt River) is the only flowing river; its water is sweet in the upper reaches, then turns brackish, and is quite saltish by the time it enters the sea. There are several saline lakes in this arid region, of which the Sambhar lake is the largest. To the north of Jaisalmer, a number of playa lakes known as Ranns occur in basins rimmed by scarps. Though fed by centripetal drainage these lakes are generally dry. The sand dunes are usually of the barchan type, which in the Barmer region are as much as 50 to 100 m high.

The Ganga plain occupies about 3,57,000 km² and is spread over parts of Uttar Pradesh, Bihar, and West Bengal. The Yamuna flows near the western boundary of the plain for 800 km and joins the Ganga at Allahabad. Further east is the Bihar plain which is a land of rivers. The Ganga flows along its southern border, receiving on its left bank three large tributaries, the Ghaghara, the Gandak, and the Kosi. These streams are responsible for filling up with alluvial deposits a 2,000-metre deep trough at the foot of the Nepal Himalayas.

The plains in north Bengal extend from the foot of the Eastern Himalaya to the northern limit of the Bengal basin. Its eastern part is drained by the rivers joining the Brahmaputra, and the western part by the tributaries of the Ganga. Further south lies the Barind plain which is the older delta of the Ganga formed during the Pleistocene time and later uplifted and eroded into terraces. The Bengal basin is mainly composed of the Ganga delta. It is a low flat country which would be completely submerged if the sea level rose by only about 6 m. The alluvial plain is almost at the base level of erosion in the Sunderbans, and is traversed by a network of estuaries and channels.

The alluvial plains of Peninsular India will be described when dealing with the east and west coasts of India.

Terraced plains. Most rivers in the Himalayan region have built plains in high altitudes and later dissected them into terraces (*Plate 14*). The Indus in Kashmir, the Sutlej in the Punjab

Himalaya, and the Ganga in the Kumaun Himalaya, have cut into such terraced plains at many places.

Lacustrine plains are common on the Himalayas and other mountains. The Vale of Kashmir and the Imphal basin are excellent examples of ancient lakes which have been filled up and later uplifted to their present position.

The Kashmir valley, which is one of the most beautiful and picturesque spots in India, is 150 km long from north-west to south-east, with a width of 80 km, and an average elevation of 1,700 m. The valley is enclosed by a ring of mountains, the Pir Panjal in the south, and a northerly branch of the Great Himalaya in the north. The river Jhelum flows across the valley from south to north.

In the central part of Manipur hills lies the large Imphal basin which is 50 km long and 30 km broad, surrounded on all sides by high mountains. This plain which is the bed of an old lake has centripetal drainage.

Glacial plains. The Ladakh plain in the northeastern part of the Kashmir Himalaya, lies to the east of the Shyok river and north of the Chang Chenmo river. In this flat valley there is abundant evidence of former glaciation.

Typical examples of *piedmont plains* are found at the foot of the Himalayas. The piedmont plains in the Punjab are dissected into terraces by streams which remain dry during most of the year.

Arid plains which are generally rocky are present west of the Aravalli, especially near Jaisalmer town. *Lava plains* occur on the Konkan coast in western India. *Pediplains*, caused by the recession of hills, are common in South India. *Coastal plains* of the emergent type with lagoons and backwaters, are found on the coasts of Peninsular India. Peneplains formed in earlier geological ages and later uplifted are seen on some hill-tops such as on the Nilgiri and Shillong hills.

PLATEAUS AND THEIR ORIGIN

Plateaus are highlands with large summit areas of broad flattish surfaces. Usually there is an abrupt rise or fall from the surface of a plateau to the adjacent land. The term *highland* is entirely relative, for many plateaus are higher than some mountains, while many plains are higher than some plateaus. The surfaces of plateaus may be like those of plains—very flat, rolling or hilly. They are often so dissected by streams that it is difficult to recognise their original plateau characteristics.

Diastrophic plateaus. All the highest plateaus of the earth are the direct products of diastrophism. After their uplift they have been modified by the agents of erosion, and in many cases by volcanism and minor earth movements. They may be classified as (1) *intermontane plateaus*, (2) *mountain border plateaus*, and (3) *domed plateaus*.

Intermontane plateaus are very high and large, with surfaces exhibiting a variety of topographic features. The Plateau of Tibet is an excellent example. This great plateau has an area of about 12,00,000 km² with an average elevation of more than 4,000 m, with many parts rising to more than 6,000 m above sea level. It is bounded by the Kunlun Mountains, the longest mountain system in Asia, and the mighty folded mountains of the Himalayas, Karakorum, and Tien Shan.

Many plateaus border mountain ranges, their present position being due to the same uplift that raised the mountains. Again, some extensive regions are uplifted by folding and faulting into broad domed plateaus.

Volcanic plateaus. Some of the largest plateaus are built up by the successive outpourings of lava from fissure eruptions. Such *plateau lavas* are usually made of basalt. A good illustration of this type is the plateau formed by the Deccan Traps. Smaller degraded plateaus are formed by resistant lava caps that protect the land from erosion and maintain its high elevation after the surrounding land has been worn away.

Erosional plateaus. Low plateaus are formed where streams have cut away portions of high plains, leaving broad, nearly flat highlands between the valleys.

Plateaus, like mountains, are attacked by weathering and may be found in all stages of dissection by streams and other erosive agents. When not much dissected, their flat surfaces look like plains in surface topography. If they are highly dissected, the characteristic plateau surfaces are largely removed and narrow ridges, deep canyons, and even hills and valleys are left in their place. With continued erosion, plateaus become less rugged in relief, and they are finally worn down to peneplains.

PLATEAUS OF INDIA

Peninsular India, except for its coastal plains, can be considered to be a vast plateau. The main features of plateau landscape are extensive flat or rolling plains dotted with conical or rounded hills, situated at an elevation ranging from 300 m to 900 m, and bordered by scarps.

The Malwa plateau in Madhya Pradesh occurs to the north of the Vindhya and is composed of extensive lava flows. There are rolling plains separated by flat-topped forested hill ranges.

The Vindhya plateau is situated south of the Malwa plateau, and is composed mainly of fluvio-marine deposits of probably Cambrian age, which has been uplifted and peneplaned several times since then. In structure it is a flat-topped syncline with very striking east-west erosional scarps formed of resistant quartzites.

The Chota Nagpur plateau lies to the west of the Bengal basin, the largest and most typical part of which is the Ranchi plateau, the average elevation of its upper part being 700 m. Monadnocks of rounded massive granite, and somewhat elevated terraces of older flood plains are characteristic of this peneplain. The plateau is deeply dissected along its borders giving rise to steep escarpments. In the western part of this region, there are mesa-like plateaus which are remnants of an older extensive peneplain.

South of the Narmada river there are several high plateaus. Mention may be made of the Betul plateau and the central lava plateau in the Satpura rising to a height of 1,200 m.

The Deccan plateau is the largest plateau in India. It covers an area of 7,00,000 km², and slopes eastwards and northwards. The northern and eastern boundary may be defined by the 300-metre contour line. The Western Ghats form the western boundary. The part of the Deccan plateau in Maharashtra State is formed of plateau basalt. The valleys of the Godavari, Bhima, and Krishna rivers are flanked by flat-topped steep-sided hills. In Andhra Pradesh, the plateau is formed mainly of Precambrian gneisses. The topography is characterised by rounded hills and rolling plains.

The 600-metre contour line may be taken as the boundary of the Mysore plateau which is a well-marked feature of the topography of India. This plateau abuts against the Western Ghats, and is bounded on the east by the Eastern Ghats. The Nilgiri is situated along its southern boundary. B. L. Rice writing in the *Mysore Gazetteer* in 1897 has given the following graphic description: "From the gigantic head and shoulders as it were of the Nilgiri group which commands the southern frontier, are stretched forth like two arms in a northwest and northeast direction respectively, the Western and Eastern Ghat ranges, holding within their mighty embrace the mountain-locked plateau of Mysore." Physiographically, the Mysore plateau can be divided into the Malnad and the Maidan. Malnad is the hilly area bordering the Western Ghats, and has an average width of 35 km and a mean elevation of 1,000 m. It is eroded into steep hills and deep valleys, and is covered with dense forests. The Maidan is formed of rolling plains with low granitic, gneissic, and schist hills.

CHAPTER IX

STRUCTURE OF THE EARTH'S CRUST

DURING the course of geological history, the earth's crust has experienced both large and small scale movements due to the effects of diastrophism. Evidences of such disturbances are very well seen in mobile belts. Sedimentary beds which once were horizontal are intensely disturbed with the result that they may be folded, crumpled, and fractured.

The term *structure* is used to signify the shapes and attitudes which rock-masses exhibit after they have been affected by earth-movements. In order to understand the structure of an area, it is necessary to prepare a *geological map*. The different kinds and relative ages of rocks which are seen on the surface of the land in that area are represented on such a map. Generally the topography is also shown by means of contours so that one gets a three-dimensional idea of the rock-masses.

When the rocks of the earth's crust are disturbed they will, according to the intensity of the force, either bend or break, with the production of *folds* or *fractures*. Since geological structures considerably influence the development of land-forms and scenery, a description will now be given of some of the more important types of structures.

Most sedimentary rocks were originally deposited on flat or gently inclined surfaces and, therefore, if great thicknesses of strata are found in inclined positions, it is obvious that they must have been tilted by movements which took place after the beds were deposited (*Plate 5*). In order to prepare an accurate geological map and elucidate the structure, it is important that the attitudes of such inclined beds should be carefully determined. This is done by measuring what is known as the dip of a bedding plane.

The term *dip* is used to indicate the maximum angle that a bed makes with the horizontal and the direction of the downward slope of the bed. The angle of dip is measured with a clinometer, and the dip direction by a compass. A bed which is in a horizontal position has no dip. The *strike* is the direction in which a sloping bed intersects a horizontal plane. The direction of strike is always at right angles to the direction of dip.

The name *outcrop* is given to any surface exposure of the bedrock. The disposition of geological strata will affect the shape of outcrop at the surface of the land. Horizontal beds make very large outcrops where the land-surface is almost flat. In undulating country, the geological boundaries of such beds will be horizontal and therefore, parallel to the topographical contours; the high beds which are younger will form cappings on hills, and the low beds which are older will be found at the bottom of the valleys. The outcrops which are found on the hill-tops are known as *outliers*; they are outcrops of younger rocks which are entirely surrounded by older rocks.

Hard beds resist erosion and stand up to form hills while soft beds are worn down into depressions. Such differential erosion is the cause of many characteristic landscape features. A series of gently inclined beds of different hardness gives rise to a *scarpland* type of scenery composed of asymmetrical ridges; the steep side or *escarpment* in each ridge represents the edge of the bed which has been cut back by weathering; the longer and gradually sloping upper surface is known as the *dip-slope*; and the two features together form a *cuesta*. Where the dip is steep, the ridge is known as a *hogback*.

FOLDS

A fold is a bend in a rock layer. According to the intensity of the earth forces, folds may be simple or very complex in form. The length and width of folds may vary from less than a centimetre to many kilometres.

A simple arched-up fold is an *anticline*. In a normal anticline, the beds on either side dip in opposite directions away from the crest or axial plane of the fold. Due to the tension developed during their formation, the tops of anticlines are generally fractured thus making them more easily eroded. Streams, therefore, cut deep valleys in the tops of anticlines.

A *syncline* is a downwarped fold, and is just the opposite of an anticline. The sides of a syncline dip towards each other (*Plate 6*). Synclines occur very commonly by the side of anticlines. After long erosion, synclinal structures often underlie hills and ridges. This is because the synclines being compressed are more resistant to erosion than the adjacent anticlines.

The flanks of a fold are its *limbs*, and the crest line or the trough line is its *axis*. The inclination of the axis from the horizontal plane is known as the *plunge*. The imaginary plane that bisects a fold is called the *axial plane*, and the axis passes through it.

When a fold has only one limb, that is, when the layers are bent in one direction only, it is called a *monocline*. In an *isoclinal* fold, the axial planes and often the limbs, are parallel or nearly so.

An *overfold* is one in which one limb is partly doubled under the other and the axial plane is inclined (*Plate 7*). If such an asymmetrical anticline is pushed right over, a *recumbent fold* is formed in which the axial plane lies in a horizontal position. When tangential compression is further increased, the rocks break and movement takes place on the gently inclined planes of rupture. Such dislocations associated with folding are called *thrusts*, and the actual planes of movement are *thrust-planes*.

Continental movements often result in broad *upwarped* or *downwarped* regions. They may extend from a few kilometres to hundreds of kilometres in length and width. The upwarped regions are *geanticlines*. *Geosynclines* are of great geological interest because they are sites of accumulation of strata many thousands of metres thick. Such sediment-filled geosynclinal basins have generally been subjected to very great lateral pressure, with the result that they are strongly folded and raised into mountain ranges. Many small folds occur within both geanticlinal and geosynclinal areas. The terms *anticlinorium* and *synclinorium* are used to designate, respectively, large and complex anticlinal and synclinal structures.

JOINTS

All consolidated rocks are traversed by cracks or fractures. Where there has been no displacement of the walls, the fractures are known as *joints* (*Plate 8*). They may be vertical or inclined at any angle. When fractures run through the rocks in several directions, they give rise to *joint systems* or *patterns*. Where the rocks are uniformly divided by joint systems, cubical or rectangular blocks are formed resulting in what is known as *mural jointing*. Joint faces are often remarkably smooth and straight for long distances, particularly in fine-grained hard rocks.

Joints are formed in different ways. Many result from earth movements and may be classified as *tension, compression* or *shear joints*. Both lava flows on the surface of the land and intrusions such as sills and dykes contract on cooling and develop very regular joint systems, resulting in what is known as *columnar structure*. The Deccan Trap flows near Bombay exhibit good columnar jointing. (*Plate 3*). *Sheet jointing* is sometimes well developed in massive rocks like granite. Such joints divide the rocks into crude sheets roughly parallel to the surface of the earth.

FAULTS

A fault is a fracture or fissure in the earth along which one side has moved with reference to the other side. The surface along which the movement takes place may be vertical or inclined at any angle. Faults are closely related to folds, and any type of fold may pass into a fault. Faults represent zones of weakness in which movements may occur repeatedly during long periods of time. When this happens, they are known as *active faults*. Earthquakes are common in such faulted zones.

The *fault plane* is the surface along which movement takes place. The *downthrow* side is the side that has been moved down relative to the other side, which is called the *upthrow* side. The *hanging wall* is the upper wall of the fault, and the *foot wall* is the lower wall, when the fault plane is not vertical. Many fault scarps have highly polished rock surfaces called *slickensides*.

A *normal fault* is one in which the hanging wall is on the downthrow side.   A *reverse fault* is one in which the hanging wall is on the up-throw side. A *graben* or *rift* is a block of the earth's crust, bounded on opposite sides by normal faults, which has been sunk relative to the surrounding blocks, whereas a *horst* is a block of the earth's crust which has been elevated relative to the blocks on either side. Grabens and horsts are generally long in comparison with their widths.   Frequently, they are of such magnitudes as to cause con-spicuous topographic forms.

If a considerable fault movement should suddenly take place, a cliff or steep slope, called a *fault scarp*, develops on one side of the fault.   Fault scarps are a characteristic topographic expression of faults which have reached the surface of the ground.

Given time, erosion reduces the land surface and all effects of the original fault may be removed, unless rocks of very different hardness were brought together by the faulting when a remnant of the ancient fault can be seen in the present topography giving rise to a *fault-line* scarp.   Both fault scarps and fault-line scarps recede due to erosion, and new cliffs somewhat parallel to the original scarps are formed which are, however, at some distance from the trace of the fault which is often hard to find since it is usually covered by the weathered debris derived from the retreating scarps.

Many valleys have been carved out by streams along faults because the work of erosion is, as a rule, more easily accomplished along such lines of weakness in the rocks.

CHAPTER X

EARTH HISTORY

GEOLOGICAL RECORD

WE HAVE so far been dealing with the general nature of geological processes and with the rocks and structures produced by them. Those are the facts on which the geological history of a region is based. Any study connected with history is also concerned with time. It is necessary, therefore, that the sequence of events in the earth's history and development should be determined, and the order in which various geological phenomena took place reconstructed.

One of the fundamental principles of earth science is that the present affords the key to understanding the past. This gave rise to the concept of *uniformitarianism*, in accordance with which a person trying to unravel the past history of the earth can get a clear understanding of former events by observing the natural processes which are in operation at the present time.

Another important principle is that the rocks of the earth's crust record an orderly succession of events, and that they could be arranged in a definite sequence with the oldest rocks at the bottom and the youngest at the top. This was made possible by the recognition that rocks formed at a certain period of earth history are characterised by a particular set of fossils. *Fossils* are the remains or traces of plants and animals which have been preserved in rocks. Since different types of organisms have succeeded one another in time, only rocks formed during the same age could contain identical or closely similar sets of fossils. By the application of this principle, widely separated rock deposits were correlated, and scattered pieces of evidence relating to earth history were arranged in their proper chronological order.

When sedimentary beds are deposited layer upon layer without any interruption, they are said to be *conformable*. However, the succession of sedimentary rocks is nowhere complete. Often there are pauses between depositions. These intervals of time may be brief or prolonged. When there is a long break in deposition, a part of the sedimentary sequence is missing. When an area of sedimentation is disturbed by earth movements an interruption takes place in deposition. The beds are tilted or folded and pushed up above sea level. The uplifted beds are eroded and if this area again goes under water, new sediments are deposited discordantly on the eroded edges of the tilted or folded beds. The uneven surface which separates older and younger series of beds arranged in this way is called an *unconformity* (*Plate 9*).

The *sequence* of beds arranged in order from the oldest to the youngest is known as the *stratigraphical succession* which is the basis for the interpretation of the history of deposition in a particular area. By fitting together the sequences from many different areas and including both igneous and metamorphic rocks, a *geological column* can be established which may be described as the history of the earth inscribed on stone. This stupendous column is composed of rocks which have a total thickness of nearly 150 km.

GEOLOGICAL TIME

The course of earth history has obviously taken a long period of time. Geological time is so vast as to be almost meaningless in relation to man's meagre measurement of time. In order to comprehend the enormous span of earth history, it is necessary to divide it into smaller units and set up a stratigraphical time-scale. Two sets of terms are employed—one for the time intervals, and another for the strata that were deposited during those time intervals. In order of increasing measure of time, the terms Age, Epoch, Period, and Era are used for the geological time units; the corresponding stratigraphical time-rock units are Stage, Series, System, and Group.

The earliest undoubted fossils are recognised in rocks which are 600 million years in age. This long period of time can be divided into three or four great *eras*. Working backwards in time they are the Cainozoic (modern life), the Mesozoic (intermediate life), and the Palaeozoic (ancient life). Because of its long duration, the Palaeozoic is often divided into two eras, the Upper Palaeozoic and the Lower Palaeozoic. The Cainozoic era is also known as the Tertiary, the Mesozoic as Secondary, and the Palaeozoic as Primary. Each era is further divided into a number of *periods* which are distinguished by smaller differences in the fossil assemblages. The deposits of each era constitute a *group*, and of each period a *system*.

It is difficult to classify the rocks which are older than the Cambrian. For all practical purposes the Precambrian rocks can be considered to be unfossiliferous. Some of these rocks do contain very primitive fossils which can hardly be used for purposes of classification. Radiometric dating has shown that some of the oldest rocks are 3,500 million years old. The enormous span of Precambrian time comprises several eras.

The general scheme of classification of the Geological Record is given in Table 2. The geological time-scale adopted is that given by Holmes as revised in 1959.

TABLE 2

GEOLOGICAL TIME-SCALE AFTER HOLMES (REVISED IN 1959)

Eras	Periods and Systems	Duration of Period	Total from beginning
1	2	3	4
		(Millions of Years)	
CAINOZOIC	QUATERNARY		
	Recent	2 or 3	2 or 3
	Pleistocene		
	TERTIARY		
	Pliocene	9 or 10	12
	Miocene	13	25
	Oligocene	15	40
	Eocene	20	60
	Palaeocene	10	70

1	2	3	4
MESOZOIC	CRETACEOUS	65	135
	JURASSIC	45	180
	TRIASSIC	45	225
PALAEOZOIC	*UPPER PALAEOZOIC*		
	PERMIAN	45	270
	CARBONIFEROUS	80	350
	DEVONIAN	50	400
	LOWER PALAEOZOIC		
	SILURIAN	40	440
	ORDOVICIAN	60	500
	CAMBRIAN	100	600

PRECAMBRIAN ERAS : formerly described as
PROTEROZOIC
ARCHAEOZOIC or
EOZOIC

(The term ARCHAEAN refers to the oldest known
Precambrian crystalline rocks of a region and has no
other age significance).

UNDATED INTERVAL
Undated interval 3,400-4,500 million years ago.
ORIGIN OF THE EARTH'S CRUST
Origin of the Continental Crust about 4,500 million
years ago.
ORIGIN OF THE EARTH.

GEOLOGY OF INDIA

A striking feature about the physical geography and geology of
India is that the sub-continent contains three well-defined regions.
They are (1) the Peninsular region which is a stable block of the
earth's crust composed predominantly of very ancient Precambrian

rocks; (2) the extra-Peninsular region which is formed of great mountain ranges composed mainly of folded and crumpled sedimentary rocks; and (3) the Indo-Gangetic plain separating those two regions which is a downwarped portion of the Peninsular block composed of a great thickness of alluvium.

There is a marked contrast in the physiography of the Peninsular and extra-Peninsular regions of India. The Peninsula, except in some parts which have been submerged under the sea for brief periods, has in the main continued to be a land area since Precambrian times. The extra-Peninsula, on the other hand, is a mobile belt formed of a geosynclinal pile of sediments ranging in age from the Cambrian period.

According to the theory of continental drift, the Indian peninsula was part of an ancient continental mass (Gondwanaland) situated not far from the South Pole, from which it broke away and drifted northwards. The impact of this on the southern shores of Eurasia is supposed to have buckled the geosynclinal sediments there and forced them up into the lofty ranges of mountains which borders India's Asiatic front. The Deccan block has remained stable except for some epeirogenic movements, but the Himalayan region is highly disturbed and so the rocks there have been thrown into colossal folds and subject to intense crumpling and thrusting. As usual in such orogenic activity, granites have intruded the sedimentary pile and are now seen occupying the central zone of highest elevation from the peak of Mt. Everest to Nanga Parbat on the Indus.

While there is a general correspondence between the geological history as recorded in other parts of the world and India, there are certain differences especially in the location of breaks in the stratigraphic column. It is only in the Himalayan region that a classification of rock-systems in terms of European stratigraphy can be established with a fair amount of certainty.

Table 3 gives some of the more important geological formations of India and their approximate correlation with standard stratigraphical units.

TABLE 3

MAIN GEOLOGICAL FORMATIONS OF INDIA

Geological time-scale		Rock Systems of India
Indian	European	
	Recent	Newer Alluvium
	Pleistocene	Karewas of Kashmir
		Indo-Gangetic Alluvium
	Mio-Pliocene	Siwaliks
		Cuddalore Sandstones, Warkalay beds
	Oligo-Miocene	Nari and Gaj Series
	Eocene	Ranikot and Kirthar Series
ARYAN	Lower Eocene- Upper Cretaceous	Deccan Trap

	Cretaceous	Cretaceous of Trichinopoly, Central
		    Himalayas, Assam, and Narbada
		    Valley.

	Jurassic	Upper Gondwanas (Spiti shales); Jurassic of the Himalayas
	Triassic	Middle Gondwanas; Triassic of the Himalayas.
	Permian	Lower Gondwanas (Damuda Series); Permian of the Himalayas
	Permo-Carboniferous	Talchir Series; Gondwanas of the Himalayas
	Middle to Lower Carboniferous	Carboniferous of Spiti and Kashmir
	Devonian	Muth Series; Devonian of Chitral
DRAVIDIAN	Silurian	Silurian of Spiti and Kashmir
	Ordovician	Ordovician of Spiti and Kashmir

	Cambrian	Upper Vindhyans;
		    Cambrian of Spiti and Kashmir;
		    Haimanta System of Central
		    Himalayas

PURANA	Upper Precambrian	Lower Vindyans, Cuddapahs, Delhis; Dogra and Simla slates
ARCHAEAN	Lower Precambrian	Dharwars, Aravallis; Jutogh, Salkhala, and Daling Series; Shillong Series; Peninsular Gneisses; Granites.

The Precambrians of India comprise a great variety of metamorphosed igneous and sedimentary rocks, some of which probably represent the first-formed crust of the earth. Gneisses, schists, marbles, quartzites, and banded ferruginous quartzites are the principal types of rocks. They are unfossiliferous.

The *Dharwars* in the type area in Mysore State are schistose rocks which appear from below the Deccan Traps and Cuddapah rocks, and extend in bands which have a general N.N.W. strike. They are composed of ancient lava flows and sediments, associated with some igneous intrusions. Many of the components of the Dharwars are undoubted sediments which appear at some places to rest unconformably on the Peninsular Gneisses, while at other places they are interbedded and interfolded with them. The Dharwars are economically important because they contain mineral deposits such as gold, iron, chromium, manganese, and copper. The *Aravallis* of Rajasthan have been considered to be somewhat similar to the Dharwars.

After a long interval of time during which the Dharwars and Peninsular Gneisses were deeply eroded, great thicknesses of unfossiliferous slates, quartzites, sandstones, and limestones were formed. These rocks belong to the *Cuddapah* group, so named because of their typical development in the Cuddapah district of Andhra Pradesh. The Cuddapahs rest with a profound unconformity on the older gneisses and schists. Some of the rocks of this age are diamond-bearing; the famous Golconda diamond comes from these formations. They also contain workable deposits of barytes and asbestos.

Rocks belonging to the *Delhi* group have some lithological resemblances to the Cuddapahs, though they are much more severely disturbed and folded. The prominent quartzite ridges which extend up to Delhi from north-east Rajasthan are of this age.

The *Vindhyan* group of rocks consist of undisturbed almost horizontal strata which rest unconformably over the eroded surface of the Cuddapahs. Slates, shales, sandstones, and limestones are the chief rock types. Except for a few obscure traces of animal and vegetable life, this group of rocks is devoid of any recognisable fossils. The Vindhyans are famous for building stones of great beauty and durability; the Moghul palaces of Delhi and Agra, and the Government buildings of New Delhi are built of these rocks.

The formations of the *Dravidian era* (Cambrian to Middle Carboniferous) are almost entirely missing in the Deccan because this region continued to be a land area throughout this period. In the extra-Peninsular region, however, the nearly complete sequence of marine strata is present.

The *Aryan era* which comprises the rock formations from the Upper Carboniferous to Recent, is preserved fairly completely in the Peninsula, and in a perfect sequence in the Himalayan range along its entire northern border. During the Permo-Carboniferous period profound changes took place in the relative distribution of land and sea in India. The crustal movements brought under sedimentation large areas which were land masses. The northern zone of the Himalayan region came under the waters of a great mid-world Sea, the Tethys, which filled this geosynclinal trough throughout the Mesozoic era and gave rise to a continuous system of deposits from the Permian to the Eocene. In various parts of the Peninsula, the Upper Carboniferous movements produced tensional cracks resulting in the subsidence of large linear tracts between more or less vertical fissures. These basin-shaped depressions in the old gneissic land began to be filled by fluviatile deposits. As the sediments accumulated, the loaded basins continued to subside resulting in thick deposits of freshwater and subaerial sediments in which were embedded terrestrial plants and animals of the times. These Mesozoic land deposits constitute the *Gondwana system*, which are economically very important because they have given rise to thick seams of coal.

The commencement of the Aryan era marked the onset of an Ice Age, evidences of which can be found from the Outer Himalayas to Orissa in the form of glacial till, boulder-beds, and conglomerates. At the base of the Gondwana, there is found the *Talchir series* of rocks composed of boulder-beds containing an assortment of ice-scratched pebbles and large boulders embedded in a fine-grained matrix typical of the glacial deposits of the Ice Age. From these beds it can be inferred that glaciers and ice-sheets covered India from as far north as lat. 33° to lat. 20° N.

The Talchir series is overlaid by the *Damuda series* which is a thick succession of strata with interbedded coal measures which constitute the most important coal deposits of India.

The Damuda Series is succeeded by the *Middle Gondwana* beds which correspond to the Triassic system of Europe. These strata record a remarkable change in climate from the luxuriant forest vegetation of the previous age to arid desert conditions indicated by characteristic sandstone and red clay deposits.

Outcrops of *Upper Gondwana* are present at a number of localities from the Rajmahal hills in Bihar to the Andhra State. They are typically seen in the gigantic escarpments of the Satpura range and in a large outcrop in the Godavari basin.

The Indian Gondwana flora and fauna are strikingly similar to those found in parallel groups of deposits resting upon basal glacial conglomerates in Australia, Brazil, South Africa, and Madagascar. It may, therefore, be concluded that Gondwanaland continued as a continental entity from the end of the Palaeozoic to the beginning of the Cretaceous when it broke up and individual fragments drifted away in various directions to form the present day land masses of Australia, South America, South Africa, Arabia, and India.

There is no sharp stratigraphical unconformity in India between the Cretaceous and the Eocene, as in the rest of the world. From the end of the Cretaceous till the beginning of the Eocene was a period of intense volcanic activity in the Peninsula when, out of many fissures in the earth's crust, there was an immense outpouring of basaltic lava which was eventually converted into a volcanic plateau over 1,800 m in height and more than 10,00,000 km² in area. This plateau is now dissected into numerous isolated flat-topped hill-masses which is such a characteristic feature of the landscape of the Western Ghats. The weathering of these basic volcanic rocks has given rise to the black cotton soils.

Coeval with this great burst of volcanic activity, the pile of marine sediments accumulating in the Tethys since the Upper Carboniferous was upheaved in stages by great orogenic movements. The final uplift was in the post-Pliocene period which elevated the axial part of the ranges together with the outer Siwalik foot-hills, to from the present Himalayan chain.

The upper part of the Eocene together with the Oligocene, which is present in Assam and Gujarat, is economically important because it is the chief petroleum bearing horizon of India.

The *Siwalik system* (Middle Miocene to Lower Pleistocene) covers long stretches of the extra-Peninsula. This system is composed of alluvial detrital material derived from the subaerial waste of the Himalayas. A line of faults and overthrusts separates the Siwaliks from the older rocks. This system is noted for the wealth of fossil genera and species of extinct elephants, rhinoceroses, horses, giraffes, pigs, hippopotami, deer, antelopes, carnivores, and anthropoid apes.

During the *Pleistocene*, as in many parts of the northern hemissphere, there was an onset of the Ice Age in India. Everywhere in the Himalayas there is evidence of extensive glaciation up to the altitude of 1,800 m., while glacial drift and terminal moraines cover hill-sides and valley-floors down to altitudes of 1,400 m. In the rest of India, the evidence of the Ice Age was only indirectly felt by a great lowering of temperature and in increased rainfall. The most important Pleistocene geological formation is the Indo-Gangetic alluvium (1,800 m thick in some places) filling the great depression between the foot of the Himalayas and the edge of the Vindhya-Kannanur range, a depression which was created as a concomitant of the Himalayan uplifts of the Tertiary time.

CHAPTER XI

SCULPTURING OF THE EARTH'S SURFACE

THE ENDLESS diversity of landscape which is present on the surface of the earth is produced by the action of certain agents like water, wind, and earth movements on materials which constitute the crust. The appreciation of landforms is greatly enhanced if one understands the way in which they originated, and the successive stages through which they evolved before they finally took their present form. There are some factors like the length of time during which the natural forces have acted, and the geological character of the rocks that have been sculptured, which influence considerably the type of landscape developed in any region.

WEATHERING

Weathering is a comprehensive term used to describe the processes by means of which rocks are mechanically disintegrated and chemically decomposed. By the action of weathering, rocks at or near the surface break up, decay, or crumble. Soil is the end product of rock weathering. Sooner or later the products of weathering are removed from their place of formation, by winds which blow them away as sand or dust, by rain which washes the surface away as mud and feeds the rivers, and by glaciers which carry away rock debris as morainic material. Winds, rivers, and glaciers are, therefore, known as transporting agents. The destructive processes due to the effects of the transporting agents are described as *erosion*. Rock weathering is essentially a static process which involves little or no transport of the resulting products except by gravity, whereas erosion is the natural removal and transportation of rock material. Both sets of processes co-operate in wearing away the land surface, and their combined effects are known as *denudation*.

The rate of weathering depends upon the nature of the rocks and the weathering agents which operate upon them. The agencies of weathering are mechanical, chemical, and organic. The materials ultimately produced are broken fragments of rocks and minerals, residual decomposition products such as clay, and soluble decomposition products which are removed in solution.

Mechanical weathering is mainly a physical change in which materials are disintegrated by frost action, temperature changes, and organisms.

In cold regions where temperatures fall below freezing point, the alternate freezing and thawing of water effectively breaks up rocks. Most rocks contain not only numerous natural fractures called joints but also small crevices, fissures, and pores, which are generally filled by surface water. Since water expands on freezing it exerts a strong wedging action. Repeated freezing and thawing of water which fills these openings, mechanically breaks up even the hardest rocks into smaller and smaller pieces. This type of weathering is known as *frost action*. Steep mountain slopes and cliffs are particularly susceptible to this type of disintegration. The fractured fragments fall to lower levels and accumulate there as *talus* slopes or *screes*.

In arid regions the rocks exposed to the blazing sun become highly heated with the result that a thin outer shell expands and gets loosened from the cooler layer below. This process is reinforced by the cooling effect of sudden rain falling upon hot rocks. Also, most rocks consist of two or more kinds of minerals each of which expands at a different rate; this sets up minor stresses and strains which tend to pull apart the minerals and break up the rocks.

Due to a combination of causes usually including temperature changes, the outer portions of rocks peel off in small or large slabs or sheets. This process is called *exfoliation*, and is especially effective in uniform massive rocks with fairly large mineral grains. The effects of exfoliation are well seen in many granite hills in India. The bare steep-sided *inselbergs* (from the German meaning 'island mountains') of granite afford good examples. Chemical and temperature changes gradually round off the sharp edges and projecting knobs, and the hills become dome-shaped with increasingly steep sides as time goes on (*Plate 10*).

A remarkable example of the efficacy of rain erosion is seen in what are known as *earth pillars*. The ideal condition for their formation is when a soft clay or shale bed is capped by a hard layer, or contains resistant boulders. The continued action of rain produces pillars of the soft clays, each pillar being protected on the top by a slab or boulder of hard rock. Examples of earth pilllars can be seen in the alluvial terraces in the Central Himalayas in Spiti.

Both directly and indirectly, plants contribute much towards rock disintegration. Growing roots and trunks of plants widen cracks and often wedge rocks apart. Burrowing animals such as earthworms, rodents, and termites, aid the action of weathering agents by bringing fresher materials to the surface and by allowing more ready access to such agents for further disintegration. Man has also helped in preparing the land for erosion by deforestation, permitting forest fires, faulty procedures of ploughing in sloping grounds, and by indiscriminate methods in mining.

Chemical weathering comprises changes in which the minerals of rocks are decomposed, dissolved, and loosened by the action of water, oxygen and carbon dioxide which are important constituents of the lower atmosphere; also, by organisms and the products of their decay. In nature, the physical, chemical, and biological agents work together in attacking rocks.

The important chemical changes that take place during weathering are solution, oxidation, hydration, and the formation of carbonates. Only a few minerals such as quartz and muscovite mica resist decomposition. Some like the carbonate minerals are entirely removed in solution. Most silicate minerals break down into relatively insoluble residues like clay.

Chemical weathering causes disintegration of rocks by loosening the cohesion between minerals and by the formation of solutions which are washed away by the rain, thus rendering the rock porous and ready to crumble.

The chemical weathering of fine-grained and homogeneous rocks which are traversed by rectangular joints leads to the formation of rounded cores of unaltered rocks surrounded by concentric shells of decomposed material somewhat like the outer wrappings of an onion. This is because the depth of decomposition is greater at corners and edges than along the flat surfaces. This process is called *spheroidal weathering*. Very good examples are found in the Deccan Trap country.

In moist climatic regions, rain water sinks deep into the rocks and hence, weathering proceeds to a considerable depth. In some parts of the Western Ghats weathering may extend to depths of 20 to 30 m. Under certain conditions, specially where a heavy rainfall season alternates with a dry season, the products of weathering include hydroxides of aluminium and iron, silica, and various carbonates and sulphates. Most of these are washed away by rain water, but the hydroxides of aluminium and iron are left behind as insoluble residues at or near the surface and form a reddish brown deposit called *laterite* (derived from the Latin word *later* meaning 'brick'). In many parts of the Western Ghats region, and in some other places, laterite is cut into bricks and used extensively as a building material. It is very useful because the bricks after they are cut from soft laterite become quite hard on exposure. The variety of laterite which is rich in aluminium is known as *bauxite*, which is an important ore of aluminium.

In many places there is a superficial layer of loose broken up material called *waste-mantle* or *regolith* which rests upon the bedrock of the earth's crust. This mantle of waste-rock may be either *residual*, that is, remaining where it was formed by processes of weathering, or *transported*, when some transporting agent such as water, wind, or glacier, has carried it to a different place.

Weathering processes function very differently under varying climatic conditions. In *cold* climates, mechanical weathering is very important. In *temperate humid* climates, all the weathering processes are exceedingly active. In *dry temperate* climates, mechanical weathering is somewhat more evident than chemical work. In warm and *hot humid* climates, chemical weathering is far more important than mechanical weathering because heat and moisture greatly facilitate leaching and solvent action. In *dry hot* climates mechanical weathering predominates.

FORMATION OF SOIL

The physical and chemical processes of weathering co-operate in close association with biological processes to produce *soil* which is the surface layer of the mantle of rock-waste. Of all processes none are so important as those which help to produce soil, since all forms of plants and animals depend directly or indirectly on soil for their existence. Since these processes are influenced by climate, the resulting soils also vary with the climate. The nature of the soil depends particularly on the kind of bedrock from which the soil was formed.

Two general kinds of soils can be recognised, namely, residual and transported. *Residual soil* is more or less dark in colour because of admixture with decomposing organic matter (humus). This grades downward into *subsoil* which contains fragments of partly decayed rock, and little or no vegetable matter. The subsoil in turn passes gradually into partly decayed *rotten rock*, and then finally into the underlying unaltered *fresh rock*. Old residual soils are often so changed by chemical decomposition that it is difficult to recognise the original nature of the parent rock and such soils are said to be *mature*.

Transported soils are those which have been removed from the rocks on which they were formed. These soils may have been moved only a short distance by gravity or soil creep, or they may have been carried any distance up to hundreds of kilometres by glaciers, streams, or wind. *Alluvial soils* are those which have been carried by streams and deposited by them on land. Youthful swift streams carry pebbles, gravel, sand, and silt, while old slow-moving streams transport finely divided rock material. Alluvial soils are found chiefly on the flood plains of rivers and in deltas. The classic example of the Indo-Gangetic plain well illustrates the formation of both alluvial and deltaic soils. *Glacial soils* have been carried by glaciers as debris and deposited as moraines; such unstratified deposits are known as *drift* or *till*. Some drift is composed chiefly of fine material such as clays and rock flour; in other places boulders of varying sizes are abundant. The rock fragments are *angular* as opposed to the rounded ones of alluvial deposits.

Because of the diversity of minerals and rocks which give rise to soils, and the varying conditions under which the materials are weathered, there are many kinds of soils. *Sand* is composed of quartz grains and makes too light a soil for many plants as it is too porous to hold water. *Clay* consists largely of very finely divided kaolin; as a soil it is too impervious. A mixture of sand and clay makes *loam* which is very good soil. *Marl* is a combination of clay and limestone, that is carbonate of lime. *Muck* is a very dark soil exceedingly rich in decayed vegetable matter. These differences are well marked in young soils and in temperate regions. In mature soils, some ingredients are continuously leached out, while others are concentrated. For instance, the accumulation of humus depends on the excess of growth over decay, a condition which is related to the climate. The composition of the soil thus gradually becomes different for each climatic region. The colours of the soils are mainly due to the abundance or paucity of various iron compounds and humus. Black soil has developed equally well in the Russian steppes from such different rocks as granite, basalt, loess, and boulder clay. On the other hand, granite gives grey soils (podsols) in temperate regions, black soils (chernosem) in the steppes, and reddish soils (lateritic earths) in tropical regions.

SOILS OF INDIA

The soils of India are generally very old and fully matured. To a great extent, the formation of soils depends on the climate, especially the seasonal distribution and amount of rainfall. The soil temperatures in India are 10° to 20°C higher than those prevalent in temperate zones. The chemical reactions involved in the formation of soils are consequently much more intense, and therefore, rock disintegration is rapidly followed by chemical decomposition.

The *soils of the Indo-Gangetic plain* are mainly alluvial, being composed of the debris brought down by rivers from the Himalayas. They consist mostly of loam which is a mixture of clay and sand,

and form the most fertile region in India. Most of the *soils of Peninsular India*, on the other hand, have been formed in the area where they are found. Their fertility depends on the chemical constituents of the rocks from which they are derived.

The soils of India can generally be classified as follows—1. Alluvial soils; 2. Black soils; 3. Red soils; 4. Laterite soils; 5. Forest and hill soils; 6. Arid and desert soils; 7. Saline and alkaline soils; 8. Peaty and marshy soils.

1. *Alluvial Soils:* The alluvial soils of the Indo-Gangetic plain are coarsest in the upper section, medium in the middle section, and finest in the lowest section of the valley. Sand, being the coarsest, naturally predominates in the upper courses of the rivers, while clay, being the finest marks the lower courses. Because of the level terrain, numerous irrigation canals have been cut throughout the Ganga valley. The alluvial tracts of Bengal are more compact, less coarse, and more moist than elsewhere, and yield good crops of rice, sugar-cane, tobacco, and jute.

The alluvial soils of the Deccan coastal strips are non-porous, clayey, and of a dark colour. They are found along the valleys and at the mouths of the important rivers of Peninsular India.

2. *Black Soils:* Black soils are present in Mysore, Maharashtra, Gujarat, western Madhya Pradesh, southern Uttar Pradesh, southeast Bihar, northwest Orissa, and western Andhra Pradesh. The most important soil in the Deccan Trap area is the *regur* or *black cotton soil*. While this type of soil has in many places been derived from basaltic lava flows, it is also a mature soil which has been produced by relief and climate rather than from any particular type of rock.

The black soils are invariably highly argillaceous and somewhat calcareous. They are very compact and tenacious, and are highly retentive of moisture. They are fertile and specially suitable for growing cotton, wheat, linseed, jowar, and gram.

3. *Red Soils:* Red soils which are characteristic of tropical regions, occur in many parts of Peninsular India. The soils vary greatly in colour, consistency, and depth. The sandy and light-coloured soils of the arid uplands yield only bajra, while the bright

red fertile loam of the plains produces a wide range of useful crops.

4. *Laterite Soils:* Lateritic soil is formed by weathering of laterite. It is red in colour and coarse, and is composed of clay and much gravel. The distinguishing characteristic of this type of soil is its acidity and, therefore, the chief agricultural problem is the correction or amelioration of this acidity. Since the tea-plant requires acidity, tea cultivation is common in these areas.

5. *Forest and Hill Soils:* The formation of these soils is due mainly to the accumulation of organic matter derived from forest growth. These soils occur in the hill districts of Assam, Uttar Pradesh, the sub-Himalayan region, and Coorg.

6. *Arid and Desert Soils:* Such soils are mainly composed of sands often with high salt content. They occur in the arid regions of south Punjab and Rajasthan, and contain very little organic matter. Such regions are generally covered by a mantle of largely wind-borne sand. The limiting factor for agriculture in such areas is mainly water, and reclamation is possible only by proper irrigation. This has been recently demonstrated in Orunda, a dreary desolate and waterless spot in the Rajasthan desert, which by irrigation has been converted into green fields of wheat, barley, mustard, rice, and grapes.

7. *Saline and Alkaline Soils:* These soils are found throughout India in all the climatic zones. Many dry tracts especially in Bihar, Uttar Pradesh, Punjab, and Rajasthan, give rise to saline and alkaline efflorescences which are harmful for crops. The saline soils contain excess of sodium chloride and sodium sulphate, while alkaline soils contain excess of sodium bicarbonate.

8. *Peaty and Marshy Soils:* Peaty soils originate in humid regions by accumulation of organic matter. These soils are black, heavy, and highly acidic. They are found in Kerala. Marshy soils are met with in the coastal tracts of Orissa, Sunderbans and some parts of Bengal, north Bihar, and southeast coast of Madras.

CHAPTER XII

RUNNING WATER

FOR MILLIONS OF YEARS atmospheric agents of erosion have been working unceasingly to reduce the land masses to the level of the seas. Water, wind, and ice are the three great agents of erosion. Of these, running water is the most important. The direct sources of stream water are rain and melting snow. On an average about 100 cm of water in the form of rain or snow falls on the land each year, which is equivalent to about 1,50,000 km³ of water. The water which is precipitated as rain runs off the slopes of the land in thin sheets, and then travels on in rills, streams, and rivers, till it reaches the oceans. It is evaporated into the atmosphere and reaches the land again as rain or snow. This is known as the *hydrological cycle*. Only about one-sixth of the quantity of water falling on land is carried by the rivers into the oceans; the major part of it is evaporated or sinks into the ground.

It is generally true that less is known of the source than of any other part of the river. The source may, as in the case of the Ganga, be from an ice-cave at the snout of a glacier just below the snow-line; or it may arise like the Narbada from a spring on the highlands of Amarkantak; or it may originate in a lake like the Sutlej whose source is in the westward overflow from the Manasarowar lake. In almost all cases, it is extremely difficult to locate the exact spot at which a river commences.

Rain water accomplishes a certain amount of erosion before it collects into streams. This is evidenced by the fact that soils are carried down slopes by the wash of the rain. This type of wear by rain is known as *sheet erosion*.

Streams differ from one another in many respects. Some are several thousand kilometres long, others are short. Some are large, others are small. Streams are closely spaced in some regions, and in others they are wide apart. One stream may carry a great load of silt, while another may be clear, most of the time.

Streams are numerous where precipitation is heavy, and few where it is light.   Faults, folds, and broad upwarps and downwarps of the land control the location of many streams.

Some streams flow throughout the year because they rise in lakes or at the foot of melting glaciers, or because they flow mainly in a region where there is plenty of rain.   Such streams are known as *permanent*.   Good examples are the Himalayan rivers which, because they are snow-fed, continue to flow throughout the year. Streams which flow in semi-arid regions depend on sources of water which are seasonal and are, therefore, *intermittent*.   The rivers of central India and the Deccan are generally rain-fed and hence, the volume of water fluctuates considerably throughout the year. *Ephemeral* streams are those which do not flow continuously for even one month; they are characteristic of semi-arid and desert regions. Most of the streams of the interior drainage basins are of such an ephemeral character.   They drain towards the individual playa (temporary lake) basins or salt lakes like the Sambhar, or are completely lost in the sands and do not flow into the sea.

Methods of Stream Erosion

Streams carry rock fragments of all sizes, from those of silt, mud, or sand, to pebbles and even boulders.   This is known as the *load*, and constitutes the grinding tool by means of which streams accomplish mechanical erosion.   The mechanical wearing away of the sides and floor by the rubbing and bumping action of the rock fragments carried by the stream is known as *corrasion*. Rapid corrasion takes place where a stream containing plenty of angular rock fragments flows fast over relatively soft rocks.   The well-rounded and often highly polished pebbles and boulders that are found on stream beds bear witness to the considerable amount of corrasion that has taken place.   Corrasion is mainly responsible for the deepening of valleys by streams.   The drilling of *pot-holes* is a very important method of down-cutting.   Pot-holes are formed in solid rock through the grinding action of sand and pebbles which lodge in slight initial depressions and are swirled around by the eddying waters. Vertical holes are cut deeply into the rocks as the water plunges in and keeps the pebbles and boulders in action by its spiral motion.

River waters carry large quantities of material in solution. The soluble minerals are extracted both from the rock fragments that are carried by the stream, as well as from the rocks of the bed and banks along which the stream flows. Such a chemical action that is carried on by running water is called *corrosion*.

The mere impact or pressure of running water often effects a considerable amount of erosion when it flows over soft or loose material, or where hard rocks are traversed by numerous joints. The *hydraulic action* caused by the pressure of flowing currents is capable of dislodging blocks of rock which are divided by planes of stratification or systems of joints.

It is estimated that 8,000 million tons of material are annually transported to the sea by rivers from drainage basins having a total area of 105 million km². This corresponds to the removal of one metre of the land surface in 30,000 years. The average rates of denudation, however, vary widely from basin to basin.

TRANSPORTATION BY STREAMS

The visible mechanical load transported by a stream consists of material carried in suspension and pushed or rolled on the bottom; the invisible chemical load is the mineral matter carried in solution. Even a small increase in the velocity of a stream greatly increases its transporting power; that is the reason why a river in flood is devastating in its destructive effects.

A stream which has sufficient velocity and volume to transport more material than is added to it by its tributaries, is able to cut down and deepen its channel, that is, to *degrade* it. As this process of downcutting advances, the gradient of the bed of the stream becomes gradually reduced, till the stream reaches a stage in which its whole energy is spent only in transportation and then there is no degradation. When a stream acquires more load than it can carry it is said to be *overloaded*. Such a stream is unable to cut down its channel, but by depositing part of its load, it actually builds up its channel, that is, *aggrades* it.   Many mountain streams are so loaded by debris brought in by steep-gradient tributaries that their valley floors are raised instead of deepened as one might expect in regions of high relief.

When a condition is reached in which the stream's load and transporting power are approximately balanced, the stream is said to be *graded*.   Such a stream neither degrades nor aggrades, but is just able to carry the load supplied to it by its tributaries.

The *base level* of a stream is the lowest point to which it can erode its channel.   The stream cannot deepen its bed below this level. Temporary base levels are caused by lakes, resistant rock-masses, and any barriers which hold up the downward passage of water. The ultimate base level is the ocean into which the stream must flow.

CHARACTERISTICS OF STREAMS

On any new land surface, the first streams will have their courses determined by the original slope.   Such streams whose courses are the direct consequences of the initial topography are called *consequent streams*.   On the other hand, many stream courses are not dependent on the original topography but are determined by the differential erosion of the bed rocks.   The valleys of such streams lie along the lines of the softer or less resistant rocks, and so their positions are in direct response to rock structures.   All such streams which develop independently of the original relief of the land are called *subsequent streams*.   These are often tributaries of consequent streams.   Usually subsequent tributaries develop nearly at right angles to a consequent master stream.   This is often due to the fact that consequent streams are parallel to the dip and subsequent streams are parallel to the strike.   This rectangular pattern of stream courses is known as *trellis drainage*.

Obsequent streams also are streams which have developed in certain positions by adjustments to rock structures.   After the valley development of consequent and subsequent streams, obsequent streams may form at right angles to the subsequent streams and flow *opposite* to the direction of flow of the original consequent stream. Such obsequent streams are found in regions of tilted strata where escarpments form by erosion of the land surface. Obsequent tributaries develop on such escarpments.

Streams that develop their valleys on flat-lying sedimentary rocks, or on massive rocks like granite, which have no pronounced structural features, are called *insequent streams*. Their drainage pattern being tree-like in form is called *dendritic drainage*.

Mention may be made here of one of the most extraordinary drainage patterns in the world which is found in the Himalayas. The valley of Kathmandu, the capital of Nepal, is floored with deltaic lake sediments on a basin-like depression sloping inwards towards the city. This basin is surrounded by spurs of the Middle Himalayas, and on the south by the Mahabharat range. There is only one exit for the Bagmati river which drains the amphitheatre, and that is through a deep gorge in the Mahabharat. The Upper Bagmati and its tributaries afford a most remarkable example of *centripetal drainage*. Along the line of exit, the Bagmati flows southwards towards the Ganga while only about 1.5 km to the east the Nakhu Khola flows due north to join the Bagmati just south of Kathmandu.

Many things can happen to streams after they have started to cut their valleys. They may be captured by other streams; glaciers, lava flows, or landslides may dam their valleys and form ponds, or deflect the course of the streams; the source of water supply may be cut off by crustal movements or climatic changes. The courses of streams are also changed during floods.

During the erosional history of a region, certain streams sometimes seize parts or all of other streams by a process known as *stream capture* or *piracy*. This happens when a stream under certain conditions is able by headward erosion to extend itself or one of its branches till it taps and diverts into itself part or all of the stream whose erosional conditions are less favourable. Stream capture of youthful and mature streams is common in regions of folded rocks. Also, when streams meander widely over flood plains, stream capture takes place due to lateral cutting and intersection of meanders. A stream whose upper waters have been captured is said to be *beheaded*. The beheaded stream, now containing much less water, is described as a *misfit* since its reduced size is no longer commensurate with the valley through which it flows. The deserted notch at the head of its valley becomes a *wind gap*.

The river Sharavati in Mysore State which is famous because of the spectacular Jog Falls where the river makes a shear leap of 250 m, has resulted by river piracy. A swift-flowing consequent stream having its source on the western slopes of the Western Ghats and draining into the Arabian Sea, pushed its way up the divide by rapid headward erosion and captured the well-graded mature drainage on the Mysore Plateau, which was flowing generally eastwards into the river Tungabhadra. The Jog Falls are at the head of a precipitous gorge which is about 25 km long, on either side of which there are hanging valleys from which the tributary streams join the Sharavati in minor water falls.

Many of the Himalayan rivers in their upper reaches are examples or river capture or piracy. This is due to the rapid head-erosion of the main transverse streams capturing or beheading successively the secondary lateral streams belonging to the Tibetan drainage system on the northern slopes of the Himalayas. Very good illustrations of river capture are furnished by the Bhagirathi and other tributaries of the Ganga, the Sind river in Kashmir, and the Arun in the Everest area.

Rapid head erosion and capture of lateral streams on the opposite slopes result in *hanging valleys*, where the side-valleys or tributaries are hundreds of metres above the level of the main stream into which they discharge. A good example is that of a former tributary of the Tista river of Sikkim discharging its waters by precipitous cascades into the Rathong Chu which flows nearly 700 m below.

It sometimes happens that after the course of a stream has become well established, movements of the earth, intrusions or extrusions of igneous rock may occur which ordinarily would divert the course. If the stream is strong enough to maintain its former course in spite of the deflecting forces, it is called an *antecedent stream*. The simplest case is that of a revived river resulting from rejuvenation of a region by uplift without much change in the general direction of the slope of the land. An interesting type of antecedent river is one which has kept its course through a rising barrier, even a mountain range.

There are some remarkable examples of antecedent rivers in the Himalayan region, for example, the Indus and its tributary the Sutlej, and the Brahmaputra. These rivers are obviously pre-Himalayan in origin, for they rise in Tibet well to the north of the highest peaks. The Indus when it leaves Kashmir near Nanga Parbat (8,737 m), is barely 1,000 m above its delta with precipit-ous walls on either side which rise by a series of steps to 6,600 m, the river having thus cut through 5,600 m of rock keeping pace with the uplift of the mountain range. The Indus and the Sutlej flow northwest, while the Brahmaputra flows eastwards, for long distances before they abruptly change direction *towards* the moun-tain barriers and pass through stupendous gorges cut in the bottom of V-shaped valleys.

The Cauvery in south India is an antecedent river in the Penin-sula. It originates almost at the western edge of the Western Ghats within sight of the Arabian Sea, but instead of flowing west and joining that sea, it cuts across the main range and flows across the Mysore Plateau. This part of the course is characterised by broad incised meanders, rapids, and waterfalls, features which are characteristic of rejuvenation. Shimsha and Arkavathi which are tributaries of the Cauvery, have hanging valleys with water falls due to headward erosion, the recession being as much as 7 km in each case.

Sometimes streams start cutting their valleys in rocks of certain composition and structure, and later, as erosion goes on, the streams reach and cut into the originally buried underlying rocks. The newer overlying accumulations may be sheets of lava, glacial or lake deposits, or sedimentary beds; and the old land mass which is buried under the later rocks may have its own characteristic topography, rock character, and structure. The surface of the newer formation may be quite different from that of the older, underlying formation. For instance, a series of horizontal strata with a smooth surface might be resting on top of a rugged surface of igneous rocks or on folded and tilted metamorphic rocks. Final-

ly, after the overlying rocks are worn away, the streams are found
in most unusual places, such as the crests or sides of sharply folded
anticlines, or crossing resistant rocks which in the normal course
of development they would have avoided.   When a stream, whose
course has been determined upon the newer surface, cuts through
the overlying rocks into the underlying rocks, and maintains its
course irrespective of the surface, character, and structure of the
underlying rocks, it is said to be *superimposed*.   In such cases, the
courses have been predetermined by the rocks in which they first
started to cut their valleys.   The superimposed streams often have
courses which are completely out of harmony with the structural
surroundings of the formerly buried rocks.

The streams in the region around Saugar in Madhya Pradesh
afford examples of superimposed drainage.   In this area, the
Vindhyan formations were buried beneath the Deccan Trap flows.
Subsequent erosion removed a large part of the Trap exposing to
view a mature topography of hills and valleys carved out of horizontal Vindhyan strata.   The streams which originated on the lava
plateau have continued to erode in the courses they followed on
the Deccan Trap, and the more powerful ones have cut gorges
through the Vindhyan hills.   The present drainage which originated on a Deccan Trap plateau has, with the removal of much of
the Trap rocks, become superimposed on the underlying Vindhyans
regardless of the structure of the latter.

Valley Development

Water from rainfall or melting snow collects in the depressions
and begins to run off in streams.   These initial streams carve out
gullies which gradually get deeper, longer, and wider, and finally
become valleys.   The development of a valley depends on the
original surface slope; on the climate which influences the amount
of rainfall; and on the geological structure of the rocks which
determine the varied resistance to erosion.

A valley is *deepened* by the cutting down of its floor by the erosive
action of the stream which flows in it.   The power of a stream to
cut down or degrade its valley slowly diminishes because of lessen-

ing velocity, until a limit is reached below which the stream cannot cut. The lowest level to which a stream can cut down its valley is called *base level*, which is an imaginary extension of sea level beneath the land surface. The rivers of Peninsular India have almost base-levelled their courses.

Water flowing into the upper end of a gully or valley cuts back its head by erosion. By such *head-ward erosion*, a valley is *lengthened*. The lengthening of a valley ends when a permanent *divide* or division of drainage is developed.

If a valley developed entirely by the down-cutting action of a stream, the valley would only be as wide as the stream. The result would be a gorge where the walls would be vertical. Such deep gorges are found in mountainous areas and in plateaus that have been raised high above sea level, and where the rocks cut through by the rivers are chemically resistant and mechanically strong. But most valleys are much wider than the streams which flow through them. This does not mean, however, that the streams were at one time wider or larger. The *widening* of valleys takes place because of several reasons. Loose weathered materials are washed down the valley sides by rain. Landslides often occur if the valley slopes are steep. The materials which thus fall into the beds are carried away by the streams and thus the tops and the sides of the valleys steadily become wider. Again, streams rarely run in a straight line, and in a winding course the current strikes one side of the channel with greater force than the other. In this way, the river widens its valley floor by under-cutting its banks specially on the outer side of bends. Thus, the stream is responsible for some lateral erosion and consequent widening of the valley. By a continuation of this process, a series of sweeping curves are developed which are known as *meanders*. This is typical of streams at or near a graded condition when they have relatively low velocities and little or no down-cutting power. The meanders finally become a series of loops separated by narrow necks. Sometimes the necks are cut through, and a part of the meander is isolated as an *oxbow lake*.

Generally a valley has tributary valleys which branch repeatedly

into smaller and smaller tributaries.   Such a main valley with all
its tributary valleys is known as a *valley system*.   Similarly, a main
river and all its tributaries constitute a *river system*, and the whole
area from which the river system derives water and rock-waste
is its *drainage basin*.

Normally, a tributary valley or stream is at the same elevation
as the main valley or river.   Such streams and valleys are said to
be *accordant*.   This happens because, as the level of the main stream
is lowered, the gradient of the tributary stream is increased, and the
consequently greater velocity cuts down the tributary valley to the
level of the main stream.   *Discordant* valleys are those where the
tributaries enter the main valley at a higher level.   This may be
caused by the steepening or cutting back of the sides of the main
valleys by glacial erosion or other causes.

During the development of valleys, they pass through some stages
which can be recognised by certain characteristics.   Their life-
cycle includes stages of youth, maturity, and old age.   A *young
valley* is narrow and steep-sided wth only a few short tributaries.
The valleys are V-shaped in cross section.   The stream velocities
are high.   A *mature valley* is wider, less steep-sided, and deeper than
a young valley.   The tributaries are numerous and large.   An
old valley has sloping sides and fewer tributaries than a mature
valley.   It is moderate to shallow in depth, generally with a wide
nearly level flood plain over which the river flows slowly in a
meandering course.

THE RIVER PROFILE

The long profile of a river, that is, the line obtained by plotting
elevations from the mouth to the source, begins at about sea level
and rises inland.   The profile of a youthful river is very irregular
because of the slopes and undulations of the initial surface.   Given
plenty of time in a region which has not been disturbed by earth
movements or changes of climate or sea level, the profile gets progressively modified until it approximates to a smooth curve, gently
concave to the sky, steep near the source and almost flat at the
mouth.   A river with such a profile is said to be *graded*.

PLATE 6—**Hill formed of beds of limestone folded into a syncline, Himalayas.**
(See Page 58)

PLATE 7—**Overfold in the Krol Belt, Himalayas.** (See Page 58)

PLATE 8—**Joints in granite, Mysore State.** (See Page 59) (*Photo*—C. S. PICHAMUTHU).

PLATE 9—**Unconformity: limestone bed deposited on eroded irregular surface of gneiss. Cape Comorin, Madras State.** (See Page 62)(*Photo*—C. S. PICHAMUTHU)

PLATE 10—**Steep-sided boss of granite, Rajasthan.** (See Page 72)

PLATE 11—**Narrow gorge with river flowing at the bottom between steeply rising banks, Himalayas** (See Page 89) (*Photo*—S.C. AWASTHI).

The Cycle of Erosion

The *cycle of erosion* is the period of time during which streams reduce a newly formed land mass to base level. The topography which is developed during the various stages of a cycle of erosion is known as the *geomorphic cycle*.

The terms youth, maturity, and old age have earlier been applied to streams, which with their tributaries constitute a *drainage* or *river system*. Similar terms are also applied in the evolution of topography. The topography will at first be in its *infancy*, then *youthful*; gradually it will attain *maturity*; finally, as the relief is diminished and base level is approached, the land surfaces will have become *old*.

Infancy Stage: The infancy stage is the earliest in the cycle of erosion. Very few streams are formed and they seek out the original depressions and flow down the initial slope of the land. They are typically consequent streams, and a characteristic of them is the small number of tributaries. During infancy, stream erosion accomplishes very little, but the process of sheet erosion is most effective.

Youthful Topography: In a youthful topography, there are few streams with high gradients which flow in narrow steep-sided canyons, gorges, or V-shaped valleys. Rapids and waterfalls are numerous. Lakes and swamps are also common. The streams are mainly engaged in cutting their valleys deeper. In youthful regions, the bottoms of most of the valleys and the surrounding land are well above base level.

Canyons and *gorges* are valleys whose walls are very high and steep (*Plate 11*). The most magnificent example in the world is afforded by the Canyons of Colorado in the United States of America. Canyons are formed when streams cut downward more rapidly than weathering can reduce the slope of the walls of the valley. Generally the steep walls of the canyon are composed of rocks like quartzite which are resistant to chemical weathering. Faults or joints help the downward cutting by streams, and in the maintenance of the steep walls. The rapid recession of a waterfall may result in a gorge.

Very impressive canyons occur at the headwaters of the Krishna river, northeast of Mahabaleshwar, at the edge of the Western Ghats; here the rocks involved are the almost horizontal beds of the Deccan Trap basaltic lava flows, which have been carved into steep-sided valleys which are nearly 700 m deep.

A striking example of the erosive action of the upper course of a river is seen in the Hindu Kush mountains where a tributary of the Oxus has cut a deep gorge the sides of which for a length of nearly 2 km, are nearly vertical.

Waterfalls and rapids are generally found in mountain and plateau regions. Waterfalls may be developed when a stream flows over a cliff caused either by a fault scarp or by resistant rock met with by the stream while deepening its valley (*Plate 12*). Hanging valleys also result in waterfalls. Streams cutting through plateaus built up by layers of successive lava flows often develop waterfalls. Waterfalls vary greatly in height, form, and volume of water. Where a bed of strong rock, horizontal or gently inclined upstream, overlies weaker beds, scouring of the softer beds leads to undermining and recession.

Rapids occur on the steep slopes of a stream and are often due to recession of waterfalls. They form also where streams are eroding rocks of very unequal hardness.

Mature Topography: In a mature topography the drainage is better developed. Streams with well established tributaries are more numerous. The main streams have cut their valleys to base level. There are very few lakes, waterfalls, and rapids. Hills and ridges are lower and less steep. The roughness of relief is the maximum attained in the whole cycle.

Mature topography developed in homogeneous rocks like granites and gneisses, or in horizontally bedded sedimentary rocks, can be recognised by the smooth curves of hills and valleys. A *dendritic* (tree-like) drainage pattern is developed because of the uniformity of rock composition and the absence of pronounced structural trends. This is a well-established drainage pattern which uniformly and rapidly erodes the homogeneous rocks.

In a mature topography developed on folded rocks the drainage pattern is rectangular since the tributaries meet the main streams at right angles. Tributaries to tributaries are also at right angles. Such a combination gives rise to a *trellis* drainage pattern. Considerable erosion of sedimentary rocks in folded mountain regions or even on plains or plateaus, results in long narrow ridges which are called cuestas or hogbacks. *Cuestas* are developed on rocks of low dip and have unsymmetrical cross sections, while *hogbacks* are formed on rocks of high dip and have almost symmetrical cross sections. The latter form ridges in which the dip slope is almost as steep as the escarpment. On the other hand, in horizontal beds, the cuesta becomes a *mesa* (meaning 'a table') which is a tableland capped by a resistant bed and having steep sides all round (*Plate 13*). By continued wearing-back of the sides, a mesa is reduced to an isolated flat-topped hill which is known as a *butte*.

Old Topography: In the typical regions of old topography, all the main streams are graded and they meander over their flood plains. They flow slowly and have limited carrying power. Only a moderate number of streams remain, and these flow through wide shallow valleys. The divides are low and narrow, and sometimes entirely removed by lateral erosion. Gorges and waterfalls are absent; oxbow lakes are present. The subdued landscape is gently rolling or flat. The streams have reduced the land to base level, leaving only occasional erosion remnants.

The final stage reached in a normal cycle of erosion is the *peneplain* (meaning 'almost a plain'). It represents a region of very low relief which has been reduced nearly to base level. The surfaces of peneplains are generally not perfectly flat but gently rolling with occasional low hills called *monadnocks*, which are erosion remnants whose survival is due to the superior resistance of the rocks composing them. In the development of a peneplain, the softer rocks are removed first, leaving resistant rocks to form ridges or low hills and mounds. Finally, a peneplain bevels all rocks of any composition or structure that are present in the region.

The concept of the cycle of erosion and its division into the youth, maturity and old age stages, was introduced to geomorphology more than sixty years ago by W. M. Davis. He it was who coined the term peneplain with which is associated the idea of the flattening of hillside slopes and the accompanying wearing down of divides and residual hills. In 1924, Penck contended that hillside slopes which have attained an angle that is stable for the type of rock or waste-mantle composing them, will not flatten out but would only recede without any change in the slope, that is, each slope would retreat parallel to itself. Later, Davis conceded that this view was applicable to the rocky slopes of arid and semi-arid regions but not for the soil-capped slopes of humid regions. This gave rise to the idea of a "cycle of arid erosion", according to which in semi-arid regions an inclined surface called a *pediment* was left in front of major slopes because of their parallel recession. Neighbouring pediments approaching each other from different directions, join together to form a *pediplain*.

Interrupted Cycle of Erosion: The normal cycle of erosion which ends in a peneplain, may be interrupted at any stage by other processes. In fact, interrupted cycles are much more common than completed cycles. A common but important cause of such interruption is change of level of the land due to disastrophism. An uplift of the land considerably increases the velocity of streams. Such streams cut their valleys deeper, forming new valleys below the wider, older valleys, and thus a new cycle of erosion is inaugurated. Both the streams and the topography are said to be *rejuvenated* since they have acquired the characteristics of youth. In such a case, the base level is lowered, the work to be done by erosion is increased, and the stream gets new energy to regrade its profile to a new base level. During this process of regrading, there is a marked change of slope between the newly graded profile and the old one. The place of intersection between these two profiles is known as the *knick-point*.

When rejuvenation takes place in a meandering stream, the revived stream cuts a youthful valley in the old valley floor without changing its meandering course. Such meanders are known as *incised* or *entrenched meanders*. Rejuvenation of a region can take place by uniform uplift, tilting, upwarp, or by faulting. When a river which has already developed a flood plain is rejuvenated, it cuts through the flood plain into the underlying rocks. The margins on either side are then left as flat terraces above the new level of the river. Later, the new valley is widened and a second flood plain forms within the first one. If there is another rejuvenation, a second pair of terraces may be left on the valley side. Each series of these *river terraces* corresponds to a phase of rejuvenation and valley deepening, followed by a phase of rising base level and valley widening (*Plate 14*).

Subsidence of the land also interferes with a normal cycle of erosion. The general effect of downwarp is to hasten old age by lessening the erosive action of streams. When a coastal region subsides, tide water floods the lower courses of the valleys and their streams, and they are said to be *drowned*. Such a drowned valley becomes an *estuary*, and the former tributaries of the main stream, now entering the sea by separate courses, are said to be *dismembered*.

Interruption of the normal cycle of erosion of a region is also brought about by the effects of glaciation which may superimpose the distinctive features of a youthful topography on a land area which had advanced considerably in its erosional history. Again, extensive outpourings of lava may completely bury an old erosion surface with its stream systems, while fresh stream courses are established upon the new surface of the lava fields.

DEPOSITION BY STREAMS

The conditions that cause a stream to deposit its load are exactly opposite to those that enable it to carry a load. Therefore, a reduction in gradient, volume, or velocity will result in deposition. The velocity of streams is checked when they flow from steep to gentle slopes, and the deposits spread out as an *alluvial fan*. The fan shape is developed because much of the deposition takes place at the mouth of the valley and chokes it. Minor streams are thus formed which in turn get choked. By many such repetitions, branching channels known as distributaries are formed. When the valley is clogged with debris, the flow of the stream is divided among many channels. Such an interlacing network of ever-changing, branching, and reuniting channels with islands of shingle and sand between is called a *braided stream*. Braiding is characteristic for long distances towards the mouth of the Ganga.

Flood plains of low relief are formed by deposition of alluvium on valley flats by meandering streams. They are so called because these wide flats are flooded during high water. As the valley floor is widened by meanders the slip-off slopes become nearly flat and the flood plain has only a thin veneer of mud and silt with an under-lying layer of sand and gravel covering a planed-off surface of bed-rock. Braided streams build up thicker and coarser deposits. The thickest accumulations of alluvium are, however, found filling bed-rock depressions in front of mountain ranges.

Where closely spaced streams discharge from a mountainous region across a *piedmont* (a lowland at the foot of a mountain), their deposits coalesce to form a piedmont alluvial plain. Such is the vast crescent of boulder beds, gravel, sand, silt, and clay of the Indo-Gangetic Plain, which extends from the delta of the Indus to that of the Ganga-Brahmaputra. Although the floor of this fore-deep has sunk about 2,000 to 3,000 m during Tertiary time, the depression has been filled by alluvium transported by the abundant drainage from the Himalayas.

The destination of most streams is the sea and the load carried by such streams is deposited at their mouth. These sediments accumulate in the form of flat, partly submerged, fan-shaped alluvial deposits called *deltas*. The name was first applied to the roughly triangular area at the mouth of the Nile which resembles in shape the capital form of the Greek letter *delta* ($\triangle$). An essential condition for the growth of a delta is that the rate of deposition of sediment at or just beyond the mouth of a river should exceed the rate of removal by waves and currents. A common characteristic of a delta is the presence of distributaries which wander over the delta in an ever-widening network, and so a delta-forming river always has several mouths.

Many of the great deltas of the world have been slowly subsiding while deposition of sediment has been going on. Typical deltas develop only when the rate of deposition is faster than the rate of sinking. It is known that the Indus, Ganga, and Brahmaputra deltas are subsiding. The Ganga, for example, has built an extensive delta in spite of subsidence of several hundred metres. The deltaic portion begins a little below Rajmahal near the ancient town of Gaur, now in ruins, where the first distributary, the Bhagirathi, which lower down becomes the Hooghly river of Calcutta, leaves the main stream. Such new channels develop secondary deltas of their own, and that is how the delta of the Ganga has been formed. The area of the Ganga-Brahmaputra delta south of a line joining Rajmahal with the southwest corner of the Garo Hills is no less than 1,86,500 km², and a boring to a depth of 160 m at Fort William, Calcutta, did not reach solid rock.

RIVERS OF INDIA

The rivers of India can be divided into two main groups—Himalayan rivers and rivers of the Peninsula. Of minor importance are some comparatively small coastal streams with limited catchment areas, and a few ephemeral streams of interior drainage basins which flow into playa basins or salt lakes. The Himalayan rivers are generally snow-fed and continue to flow throughout the year. The rivers of the Peninsula are rain-fed and hence their volume of water fluctuates considerably throughout the year.

Himalayan Rivers: The *Indus* rises from the springs of Sengge Khabab, about 100 km north of Manasarowar, and flows north-west for the first 250 km in Tibet before entering Kashmir. It continues to flow north-west for 550 km as far as the base of Haramosh peak (7,397 m). Then it takes a sharp southern turn cutting the Ladakh range through a terrific gorge 5,200 m deep near Bunji, and flowing for about 90 km in Kashmir, enters Pakistan. The Punjab part of the Indo-Gangetic plain is mainly due to the aggradational work of the Sutlej, Beas, and Ravi, tributaries of the Indus.

The Bhagirathi, which is the main headwater of the *Ganga*, has its source at Gaumukh, an ice cave, flows westwards for 30 km, and then turns southwards, cuts through the Great Himalaya in a deep valley, and flowing for another 140 km through the Lesser Himalaya receives at Devaprayag an important tributary, the Alaknanda. The

Alaknanda rises from the snout of a glacier just behind Badrinath, and rushes along until its course is blocked by an ice-avalanche. The river continues to flow beneath the ice for some distance, then emerges and runs along a valley which cuts through a series of tectonic ridges. At Rudraprayag it meets the south-flowing Mandakini which is fed by the melt-water of the Ghorabari glacier descending from the Kedarnath peak. Both the valleys are V-shaped, representing their youthful age, and the valley slopes are broad terraces. The combined rivers then take the name of *Ganga*. Flowing south for 70 km and cutting through the Siwaliks, the Ganga descends to the plains at Hardwar. It then flows majestically eastwards in the plains for 1,200 km, turns south and flanks the eastern face of the Rajmahal hills. It then divides into two, one branch flows into East Pakistan, and the other is the Hooghly which enters the Bay of Bengal. All through its course in the plains, the Ganga flows along a braided channel with sand banks. The Yamuna is its most important tributary on its right bank; it runs parallel to the Ganga for 800 km and joins it at Allahabad. On its left bank, the Ganga receives three of the major Himalayan rivers, the Ghaghara, the Gandak, and the Kosi.

The *Brahmaputra* rises from the snout of the Chemayungdung glacier about 100 km south-east of Manasarowar. It runs eastwards for 1,250 km in a shallow valley through Tibet, is known as Tsangpo before it sharply turns southwards, and cuts through the deep gorge of Dihang before it enters the plains. The Brahmaputra carries more water than any other river in India, but the sand-filled bed is not deep enough to carry the enormous volume of water. Floods normally begin in May with the thawing of snow in Tibet and the Eastern Himalaya, and they are augmented by the monsoon rains pouring incessantly from June to September. The rise in the level of water in the Brahmaputra prevents the waters of the tributary streams from entering the main river. This raises the water level in the tributaries causing widespread floods.

Rivers of the Peninsula: The Narmada and the Tapti, unlike the other rivers of the Peninsula, flow west. The *Narmada* rises on the Amarkantak plateau from a spring at an elevation of 1,060 m. The

PLATE 12—**Jog Falls of the river Sharavati, Mysore State. The vertical drop is about 250 m. There is a deep plunge pool at the bottom of the falls.**
(See Page 90)
(*Photo*—C. S. PICHAMUTHU).

PLATE 13—**Mesa : the flat top of the hill is characteristic. Muddanur, Andhra Pradesh.**
(See Page 91)
(*Photo*—R. VAIDYANADHAN).

PLATE 14—**River terraces on the banks of the river Indus, Kashmir** (See Page 93)

PLATE 15—**Cauvery Falls (about 100 m) at Sivasamudram, Mysore State.** (See Page ?)
(*Photo*—C. S. PICHAMUTHU).

magnificent waterfall (Marble Falls) at Bheraghat is 15 m high. After the waterfall it flows through a gorge which is 3 km long. The river finally enters the Gulf of Cambay. The *Tapti* rises on the Satpura range and reaches the Arabian Sea west of Surat.

The *Damodar* flows to the north of the Ranchi plateau in a faulted trough containing a number of Gondwana coal deposits. The three newly constructed reservoirs in the Damodar valley—Konar, Panchet and Maithon—provide water for power generation and irrigation.

The other important river that rises from the Central Highlands is the *Mahanadi*, which flows through a basin 300 m high surrounded on all sides by hills 600 to 1,000 m high. It originates on the northern edge of the Dandakaranya and flows east. The river has been dammed at Hirakud above Sambalpur, and its water, spread over 750 km^2, is utilised for irrigation and generation of power. Beyond Sambalpur the river flows through the Eastern Ghats in a gorge 65 km long. A delta has been formed before the waters reach the Bay of Bengal.

The *Godavari* rises near Trimbak in the Nasik district, and flows through a deep gorge in the Western Ghats for 20 km before reaching Nasik town. It runs for 650 km in Maharashtra before it enters the Telengana plateau in Andhra State. It cuts across the Eastern Ghats in a gorge, and flows through its own delta before draining into the Bay of Bengal.

The *Krishna* flows for 400 km before entering the Telengana country. A great dam, the Nagarjuna Sagar, has been constructed across the river in Andhra State. Near Jaggayyapeta, the river cuts across the Nallamala range and enters its delta at Vijayawada.

The *Cauvery* is the master stream of the Mysore plateau. It rises almost on the western edge of the Western Ghats in Coorg, within sight of the Arabian Sea, but instead of flowing west, it runs east crossing the Ghats. It has all the characteristics of an antecedent river. In its initial course, the river flows through an incised meandering valley. It runs generally eastwards across the Mysore plateau, and in its course there are several rapids and waterfalls. Near Kannambadi, a dam has been constructed to form the Krishnasagara, famous for the Brindavan terrace garden with its well-laid flower beds, numerous fountains, and powerful searchlights and multi-coloured lamps which transform the whole garden into a fairyland at night. Beyond the dam, the river keeps to an easterly course and branching into two arms encloses the island of Seringapatam. During most of its course in the Mysore plateau, the Cauvery has all the characteristics of a stream in its old age. The valleys are broad and shallow, the flood plains are wide, and the river sweeps in broad meanders. Then at Sivasamudram, it plunges over a precipice about 100 m high (*Plate 15*). After the falls, the river rushes along a narrow steep-sided gorge characterised by several rapids. The hardest rocks have been cut through, and huge pot-holes several metres in diameter and 10 to 15 m deep afford evidence of the great erosive power of this rejuvenated river. The down-cutting of the river is so rapid that its tributaries like the Shimsha and the Arkavathi, unable to keep pace with the corrasion of the main stream, have hanging valley ends. The river then enters the Madras State, where near Tiruchi, two distributaries flank the island of Srirangam. The principal arm of the river known as the Coleroon flows north-eastwards finally joining the sea at Devikotta.

Flowing into the Arabian Sea is the river *Sharavati*, which though small deserves to be mentioned because of the famous Gersoppa or Jog Falls in the Western Ghats which have a sheer vertical drop of about 250 m (*Plate 12*). When in flood during the monsoon season, these falls could be claimed as the greatest of the world's water-falls because of the combination of exceptional height with exceptional volume. In the dry season, however, they break up into three or four spouts of water, some of which are mere ribbon-like trickles. The Sharavati is a good example of river capture or piracy.

CHAPTER XIII

GROUND-WATER AND ITS WORK

THE water that falls upon the surface of the earth as rain behaves in three ways—some runs off into streams and rivers, some percolates into the ground, and some evaporates and returns to the atmosphere. Of the total rainfall, about 50 per cent is lost by evaporation, and the remainder is about equally divided between the run-off and percolation.

All water which occurs below the surface of the earth is called *subsurface water*, or *underground water*, or simply *ground-water*. It is present in the cracks and pores of rocks in what is known as the zone of fracture. This type of ground-water is known as *meteoric*. Fresh or salt water caught up in sediments during their deposition is called *connate*. Much of this 'fossil' water is driven away during the compaction of the sediments, and practically all of it during metamorphism. Connate waters heated up during metamorphism or by igneous activity, constitute the hydrothermal solutions which are responsible for mineral veins and hot springs. Such hot and mineral-rich water which reaches the surface from great depths is known as *juvenile*.

DISTRIBUTION OF GROUND-WATER

The depth to which water may sink underground is dependent on the pore spaces or openings in rocks through which water can move. The absolute limit of depth to which ground-water can exist is about 10 km depending upon the nature and hardness of the rocks. This is because the tremendous pressure of the overlying rocks closes all pores and cavities in the rocks beyond this depth and thus limits the downward movement of the water. In fact, very little water descends to anything like this depth, and it is probable that most ground-water occurs within a thousand metres of the earth's surface.

There are three general modes of occurrence of ground-water :

(*i*) Loose rock formations and soils are, in most humid regions, saturated with water to about 25 m below the surface. This is the main supply of water for wells.

(*ii*) Considerable quantities of water occur in certain definite layers or formations known as *aquifers*, and which are usually bounded above and below by impervious material. Water travels at a slow rate along such aquifers for long or short distances.

(*iii*) Very little ground-water is present in the hard bedrocks. Most of it occurs in joint cracks and fault fractures.

Below a certain level, all porous and fissured rocks are saturated with water. The upper surface of this ground-water is known as the *water table*. The water table is very irregular and generally follows the relief of the ground. It is generally much lower under the surfaces of hills than of valleys because the water at the higher levels travels, due to gravity, to the lower levels. The water table is lowered steadily during long periods of dry weather, and this is the reason why many wells and springs become dry. Three successive zones can often be recognized :—

(i) *Zone of aeration* which does not retain the water but allows it to percolate through to lower zones.

(ii) *Zone of intermittent saturation* which lies between the highest level reached by ground-water during wet weather, and the lowest level to which the water table sinks after a period of drought.

(iii) *Zone of permanent saturation* which extends downwards to the level below which no ground-water is met with. The depth at which the rocks are dry greatly varies according to the rock types and structures, but it is generally of the order of 700 to 1,000 m. Juvenile and expelled connate water may ascend from much greater depths.

Movement of Ground-water

Rocks are said to be *permeable* if water can pass through them freely. They may be porous like sand and sandstone; or may be non-porous like granite, but allow water to flow through them because of the presence of joints, cleavages, and cracks. Impervious or impermeable rocks are those through which water cannot easily pass. Alternations of permeable and impervious strata, especially when folded and jointed, form natural underground reservoirs of water.

The term *spring* is applied to subsurface water which gushes out from the ground. Springs may be divided, according to their mode of origin, into gravity and artesian springs. In a *gravity spring* water is not confined between impervious beds, but flows from loose materials or open passages due to the action of gravity. An *aquifer spring* is similar but its water follows a porous layer which lies between impervious beds.

Wells are holes dug or bored into the ground to a depth at which water-bearing permeable formations or fissured rocks are met with. Shallow wells dry up during dry seasons unless they touch the zone of permanent saturation.

Artesian springs or *wells* are those in which the water at depth is under sufficient hydraulic pressure to force it up to the surface. A necessary condition for such a well is an inclined or broadly synclinal permeable water-bearing formation, or *aquifer*, which is underlain and overlain by watertight impervious beds. The porous sandstones of the Himalayan foothills with their synclinal structure provide ideal conditions for artesian water. Artesian conditions are also present along the edge of the Narmada valley to the north of the Satpura range where water-bearing conglomerate beds are overlain by impervious crystalline rocks. Mining of lignite at Neiveli in Madras State has posed special problems because of the prevalence of artesian conditions. Numerous pumps have been installed for continuously pumping out the water which otherwise would flood the mines. Artesian wells are also common in Pondicherry.

Hot springs are those in which the water temperature ranges from warm to boiling point. The rise in temperature is caused by ground-water passing through recently erupted volcanic rocks which have not yet cooled to the normal temperature of the earth's crust. Water may also pass far enough below the surface to have its temperature raised by the general heat of the earth's interior, and then rise to the surface under hydrostatic pressure.

There is a group of hot sulphur springs on the bed and banks of the Sutlej at Tattapani near Simla. Many hot springs are found in the Kumaun Himalaya around the Kamet and Nanda Devi peaks. In Bihar, the thermal springs of the Monghyr district are spread over a distance of 50 km in a zone of faulting along the Kharagpur hills. Bakreswar in the Birbhum district, West Bengal, has a hot sulphur spring, the temperature of which ranges between 53°C and 72°C. There is also a hot spring at Sangameshwar on the western slope of the Sahyadri.

Geysers are springs from which a column of hot water and steam is discharged violently at intervals, the water being thrown up to heights which may reach a hundred metres. The Yellowstone National Park in U.S.A. is famous for the many geysers it contains, the most spectacular among them being the Old Faithful which erupts very regularly once in about every 70 minutes, each time sending over one million gallons of hot water in a column several metres in diameter and about 60 m in height.

A general explanation of geyser action is as follows : The geyser pipe which is filled with water extends almost vertically downward into a mass of hot lava. The water deep down in the pipe which is surrounded by lava begins to boil. Finally steam is generated which violently forces most of the water out of the geyser pipe. During each period of quiescence the whole system of cavities, communicating channels, pipe, and basin, rapidly fills up. The temperature gradually rises until the quiet phase of the cycle is disturbed by the ascent and expansion of bubbles of water vapour and hot gases, and terminated by a roaring eruption of hot water, spray, and steam.

Water entering the earth dissolves mineral matter. The amount of material dissolved depends on the distance the water travels, the kind of rock through which it has passed, the pressure, and the temperature. Where the material is relatively soluble or where the water travels far down into the earth, much material may be taken into solution and the water becomes more or less highly mineralized. Such water, when it flows out from the surface of the earth, forms a *mineral spring* which may be hot or cold. The mineral waters of such springs are often more or less medicinal in their effects.

Both through its mechanical and chemical work, ground-water greatly alters the surface of the land. This is particularly so in humid regions where the amount of water in the ground is relatively great.

MECHANICAL WORK OF GROUND-WATER

Ground-water is an important factor in causing or helping mass movements of the land. It acts as a lubricant aiding gravity or earthquakes to move rocks. Examples of mass movements are landslides, avalanches, and land creep.

Landslides are the most conspicuous of all mass movements since they involve a large volume of rock material and their topographic effects are very pronounced. Landslides are caused by a variety of causes which involve one or more of the following factors : steep slopes, lubrication by heavy rains or melting snow and ice, earthquakes, removal of support by natural causes or by man, and gravity. Such conditions generally occur on the sides of undercut slopes and cliffs, or of road, railway, and canal cuttings. Sliding takes place when bedding or cleavage planes, master joints or fault fractures dip at a high angle towards a valley or other depression.

A devastating example of a landslide was that which occurred in 1840 in the Kashmir Himalayas. An earthquake shook loose a part of the western spur of Nanga Parbat (8,877 m) where the Indus has cut a gorge 5,000 to 5,700 m deep through the great mountain range. The gigantic landslide blocked the river and dammed back the water for 65 km. The resulting lake reached a depth of nearly 350 m before it burst through the obstruction with such force that the lake was emptied in less than two days. The devastating flood tore down the valley and destroyed everything before it for hundreds of kilometres. This illustrates the fact that major landslides are often responsible for serious floods.

Snow and debris *avalanches* occur in mountainous regions where snow accumulates or where thick mantle rock becomes saturated with water on steep slopes. An avalanche of soil and loose rock is catastrophic in effect since it sweeps away trees, houses, and everything else in its path, leaving a deep narrow scar on the mountain slope, and a fan-shaped jumble of rocks, mud, and vegetation at the foot of the slope.

Mantle rock, soil, talus, and rocks have a tendency to creep down slopes. The creep is faster on steep slopes, but occurs even on very gentle slopes. Slow downhill migration of soil on hillsides, known as *soil creep*, is evidenced by fence posts getting out of alignment, curving of tree trunks near the ground, breaking of retaining walls, and displacement of railway tracks. Even the sub-soil and the upper part of the bedrock take part in the slow downhill movement. Such rock creep results in the upper ends of steeply dipping or cleaved beds curving over in the downhill direction, and hence, the apparent dip of superficial outcrops may be very different from those of the undisturbed formations.

The most important topographical effects of soil creep are (*1*) aiding erosion through sheet wash, streams, and wind, (*2*) accumulation of earth at the foot of steep slopes, (*3*) formation of low crescent-shaped scarps separated by small terraces—the whole sometimes called *stepped crescents*. These are sometimes known as "sheep tracks" though they have nothing to do with sheep.

Chemical Work of Ground-water

Pure water is a poor solvent but when charged with certain substances, especially carbon dioxide, it becomes an active solvent of limestones and other rocks. This is the reason why many minerals are dissolved in the water of springs, wells, and mines. The "hard" water of wells and springs is due to calcium carbonate, calcium sulphate, or other substances dissolved by the water during its passage through the earth.

Deposition of minerals from ground-water may be caused by such factors as cooling while water is ascending; loss of gases

PLATE 16—**Stalactites and stalagmites in limestone cave. Near Kuala Lumpur, Malaysia.** (See Page 105) (*Photo*—C.S. PICHAMUTHU).

PLATE 17—**Boulder clay: terminal moraine. 3 km from Gangotri on way to Gaumukh.** (See Page 109) *Photo*—G.V. RAO).

PLATE 18—**U-shaped valley near the source of Alaknanda rising from the snouts of Bhagirathi Kharak and Satopanth Glaciers.** (See Page 109)

PLATE 20—**Lonar Lake : considered to be**

PLATE 19—**The high sharp-pointed steep-sided pyramidal peaks ('horns') characteristic of glacier erosion, Himalayas. The glacier Nobande Sobande is seen in the foreground.** (See Page 110) (*Photo*—J. B. AUDEN).

lake, Berar, Maharashtra. (See Page 116)

PLATE 21—**Sea cliffs formed of Tertiary sedimentary beds capped by hard laterite. Varkala, Kerala State.** (See Page 130) (*Photo*—C.S. PICHAMUTHU).

PLATE 22—**Undercutting of granite block caused by the combined effect of wind erosion and exfoliation. Ganacharpur, Mysore State.** (See Page 142) (*Photo*—C. S. PICHAMUTHU).

leading to decrease of solvent power; changes of pressure during circulation; and reactions between solutions and the materials through which they pass. Calcite and quartz are thus formed as *veins* from ground-waters in joints and fissures. Many of the irregular quartz veins which occur in lightly folded rocks and in areas of regional metamorphism have been deposited in tension cracks from siliceous solutions forced out of rocks during orogenesis. *Mineral veins* especially of valuable ores are, however, not of ground-water origin, but deposited by hydrothermal solutions to which emanations of juvenile origin have contributed heat and chemically active gases.

An important result of the solvent action of ground-water, particularly in limestone regions, is the development of *caves* or *caverns*. By seeping along bedding and joint planes or other cracks in the rock, ground-water gradually dissolves the soluble rocks and creates caves which are usually irregular in size and shape. Some are like huge halls, others are vast mazes of branching passages. In some caves there are pools of standing water; in others, there are large streams of flowing water. An opening which connects a cave with the surface is called a *sink hole* or *swallow hole*.

Water seeping through the roof of caves deposits calcium carbonate in the form of stalactites and stalagmites (*Plate 16*). The deposition is brought about by the evaporation of water and loss of gases as it drips from the top. *Stalactites* are long slender pendants which hang vertically downward from the roofs of caves. *Stalagmites* are similar columns built vertically upwards from the floor by the evaporation of water dropping on it. Sometimes stalactites and stalagmites meet and form pillars.

Limestone regions sometimes present an unusual topography which has developed through the solvent action of water both on and below the surface of the land. Such regions having a rough etched surface, pitted with depressions due to solution or roof collapse, cut by numerous gullies, ravines and short valleys, and with underground drainage in place of surface streams, are said to have a *Karst topography* because of the occurrence of these features in the Karst Plateau on the east side of the Adriatic Sea.

CHAPTER XIV

GLACIATION AND ITS EFFECTS

FORMATION OF ICE-MASSES

AT THE PRESENT TIME about 10 per cent of the land surface is covered by ice. The main masses of ice are, of course, situated in the polar regions of the Arctic and Antarctic, but small masses occur in high mountains in the temperate and even in tropical latitudes.

A *glacier* is a body of snow and ice which under the influence of gravity moves slowly over the land. Glaciers originate from *snow-fields* which are stretches of perennial snow covering the landscape in areas where the winter snowfall exceeds the amount of snow that melts away during the summer. The conditions necessary for the formation of glaciers are abundant snowfall, cold temperatures, and a sufficiently low rate of summer melting, so that snow-fields continue to increase in size throughout many years.

The level up to which the snow melts in summer, that is, the lower edge of a permanent snow-field, is called the *snow-line*. Snow-line occurs at any altitude at sufficiently high latitudes and at any latitude at sufficiently high altitude. In India permanent snow lies upon the Himalayas, but it is difficult to determine the snow-line accurately because, according to Auden, the region of permanent snow passes gradually and not sharply into that which is free of snow in the summer.

Glaciers are found today in mountains at high altitudes or at lower elevations at high latitudes. Those originating in and around the heads of valleys creep slowly downwards as tongue-like streams of ice until the temperature becomes high enough to melt the ice, when it will terminate, and from its *snout* a stream of muddy water flows which may be the source of a river. Thus the Bhagirathi river has its source in the ice-cave of Gaumukh, which is the snout of the Gangotri glacier in the Himalayas beyond the peak of Kedarnath.

When glaciers overflow the land and terminate in the sea which is sufficiently deep to allow the ice to float, large masses of ice break off from the front and float away as *icebergs*.

CLASSIFICATION OF GLACIERS

Glaciers may be divided into four principal types: continental glaciers, ice caps, valley glaciers, and piedmont glaciers.

Continental glaciers or *ice sheets* are the largest of all glaciers. Such glaciers form regardless of topography on plains, plateaus, or mountains. From the centre of accumulation the ice moves slowly outward in all directions. Greenland and Antarctica are covered by thick continental ice sheets. The melting of these ice sheets would raise the general sea level by about 65 m. If this should happen at the present time much of Bengal would be flooded.

Ice cap is the covering of snow and ice on plateaus or mountains from which valley glaciers start and move in different directions.

Valley or *alpine glaciers* are streams of ice that occupy and flow down the pre-existing valleys of mountain ranges that rise above the snow line. Like streams of running water they vary in width, depth and length.

A *piedmont glacier* is formed by the coalescence of the spreading ends of valley glaciers where they flow down mountains and out upon relatively level country. It is somewhat like a lake of ice at the foot of a mountain.

MOVEMENT OF GLACIERS

The movement of a glacier is caused by the repeated processes of melting and freezing both in the snow-field and the glacial ice aided by gravity. The rate of movement varies greatly in different glaciers, and in the same glacier at different seasons. The middle and top of a glacier where friction is less, move more rapidly than do the bottom and sides. Glaciers can carry great loads of rock debris. To a great extent they glide or slide over the rock surface as is abundantly proved by the eroded and often polished and striated rock surfaces with grooves parallel to the direction of glacial movement. Unlike streams which move round obstacles, glaciers tend to erode them away, as shown by the straight smooth walls of mountain valleys from which the projecting spurs have been removed. An interesting feature of glaciers is that they can carry boulders up hill.

Lakes may be formed by the blocking of a valley by a glacier. When such a glacial dam breaks down suddenly the lake is quickly emptied and disastrous floods are caused down the valley. Many of the Indus floods are due to the bursting of a lake formed in the Shyok valley by the Chong Kumdan glacier.

A feature of glaciers is the presence of numerous gaping cracks and fissures called *crevasses* which are generally due to stretching. *Transverse* crevasses develop across a glacier when there is a pronounced convexity in the shape of the floor. Because of the greater velocity of the central portion of a glacier, stresses and strains are set up in the sides resulting in *marginal* crevasses. *Longitudinal* crevasses, which are roughly parallel to the direction of flow, develop when a glacier spreads out laterally. The ice of a glacier is often crudely stratified because the snow-field is built up of successive falls of snow, and between the falls mud often accumulates on the surface of the glacier.

Transport by Glaciers

Glaciers usually carry or drag along rock debris ranging in size from finely divided material to great boulders. This is transported by a glacier on its surface, or within it, or at its bottom. The term *moraine* is used for all such material which is collected, transported, and deposited by glaciers. The long ribbons of debris which move along the sides of a glacier are described as *marginal* or *lateral* moraines. They consist of material which has gathered on the margins of the glacier from its bordering rock walls. When two glaciers from adjacent valleys join together, the inner moraines of each unite and form a *medial* moraine on the surface. A glacier formed by the union of several tributaries may show many medial moraines. A sheet of rock debris which is deposited underneath a glacier especially during its melting and retreat is known as *ground* moraine. When it is composed of fine material with pebbles or boulders, it is called *boulder clay* (*Plate 17*). The pebbles and boulders are often characteristically facetted and striated by being rubbed and ground against the bed rock. The rock debris carried by a glacier arrives at its terminus and is dumped there when the ice melts. Where the ice front remains in a relatively stationary position for a considerable time, an arcuate ridge is built up called a *terminal* or *recessional* moraine.

Erosion by Glaciers

Pure ice can accomplish very slight mechanical abrasion. But, like running water, ice can effectively erode hard rock when it contains loose boulders and rock fragments which become its cutting tools. With the help of these materials which are imbedded in the ice, the glacier as it moves over the land removes all loose material and wears away the points and projections of the solid rocks. Rock surfaces which have been subjected to glacial abrasion are characteristically smoothened and usually more or less scratched, striated, or grooved. Such scratches and grooves are known as *glacial striae*. A rock surface with such features affords one of the best proofs of the former presence of a glacier, and the striae indicate the direction of the glacial movement. Through this mechanical abrasion, valley glaciers smooth their floors and walls, and gradually reshape the valleys through which they move from narrow V-shaped winding valleys to broad U-shaped straighter ones (*Plate 18*). This is because a glacier not only erodes the bottom of its valley but also cuts back its side especially towards its bottom. Thus the valley is deepened, its sides are steepened, and its bottom broadened. The courses are made straight because a glacier truncates by erosion the lower ends of the spurs which project alternately into the valley from opposite sides. Glacial erosion is often accomplished by what is known as *plucking*, which consists in separating from the bed rock, and pushing along, blocks of rocks which have already been more or less loosened by joint planes.

A remarkable feature of valley glaciers is their ability to erode headwards. All glaciated valleys open at their heads into amphi-theatre-shaped depressions called *cirques*. The walls of cirques are very steep, and the floor polished and striated. Cirques are likely to contain gouged lake basins which may be 30 or 40 m in depth.

Two adjoining cirques may grow at each other's expense until only a sharp-edged precipitous serrated or saw-toothed ridge remains between them. Such a ridge is known as an *arête*. Cirque-erosion from several sides reduces an upland region to a series of arêtes radiating from a central peak. If three or more glaciers cut headward until their cirques almost meet, the arêtes themselves are worn back, and high sharp pointed steep-sided pyramidal peaks called *horns* remain as the only remnants of the original broad highlands (*Plate 19*).

Stream-cut tributary valleys typically join the main stream valley at grade, that is, at practically the same level. In a glacial valley, however, the tributary valleys are discordant, that is, they join the main valley at a higher level than its bottom and are, therefore, called *hanging valleys*. This is caused by the tributary valleys having their lower ends cut clean away as the spurs between them are truncated by glacial erosion.

Drowned glaciated valleys are known as *fiords*. These long fairly straight valleys are now filled with sea water, but their glacial origin is indicated by the polished and striated steep walls, hanging tributary valleys, and other characteristic topography.

DEPOSITION BY GLACIERS

During the retreat of a glacier, the materials carried by it are left behind as a deposit to which the name *drift* is applied. The most common type of drift is *till* or *boulder clay*. This is sometimes moulded by the former ice sheets into swarms of mounds called *drumlins* which are oval in shape and generally elongated in the direction of ice movement. They are commonly half to one kilometre long.

A characteristic feature of glaciated regions is the occurrence of irregularly strewn boulders of rocks that are foreign to the place where they are now found. These ice-transported blocks of hard rocks which have been carried far from their parent outcrops are known as *erratics*. Some erratics have been moved only short distances from their original site; many have been transported at least a few kilometres, while some have been carried hundreds of kilometres. Erratics commonly rest on ice-eroded surfaces. Some have been left standing in precarious positions. These are known as *perched blocks* and are valuable evidences of glaciation in that region.

GLACIERS OF INDIA

India is a tropical country and so glaciers can be formed only in the high altitudes of the Himalayas. The snow-line is between 4,000 and 6,000 m in the Himalayas. Outside the polar regions, India has the largest area under snow, and the world's largest mountain glaciers are found in the Himalayas. The snow-fields known as *himal*, cover about 40,000 km^2; they feed the great rivers like the Ganga, the Yamuna, and the Gandak. The Karakorum Himalaya in Kashmir contains four of India's largest glaciers— Siachen (70 km), Baltoro (60 km), Biafo (60 km), and Hispar (62 km). Many of these glaciers have fast-flowing surface streams and a number of medical moraines—the Siachen, for example, has twelve medial moraines.

ICE AGES

In many parts of the world there are evidences of former glaciation on a widespread scale. Among the important evidences are abraded and striated bedrock surfaces, accumulations of drift, boulder clay, and morainic ridges. At the present time about one-tenth of the land surface is covered with ice but during the Pleistocene period this proportion was nearly one-third. It is now known that there was not just one single great advance and retreat of the ice, but that there were at least four repetitions of the glacial cycle. Each *glacial stage* was the period of a major continental ice sheet; the intervening periods during which warmth-loving plants and animals lived are distinguished as the *interglacial stages*.

The glacial and interglacial stages together constitute an *Ice Age*.

We are living in a still unfinished Ice Age which is called the Quater-
nary Ice Age, and it is not quite certain whether the future climatic
condition will be warmer or colder. A return to warmer climate
would melt the ice and result in the deep submergence of all the
seaports and lowland cities throughout the world; while another
major advance of ice would drive away man from many of the well
developed regions of the world.

An episode of great interest to us in India is the advance of ice-
sheets during the Permo-Carboniferous period. As early as 1856,
Blandford who was one of the officers of the Geological Survey of
India, discovered a boulder bed of Late Carboniferous Age at
Talchir in Orissa. This was followed up by other discoveries which
proved that Gondwanaland was repeatedly glaciated on a grand
scale at the periods during which North America, Europe, and part
of Asia had tropical or desert type of climate.

The Talchir boulder bed with its grooved and facetted pebbles,
rests on striated bedrocks. Evidences of Late Carboniferous ice-
sheets have also been found in Rajasthan and Madhya Pradesh,
and up to what are now the Himalayan foothills a *glacial pavement*
resembling recent *roches moutonnées* was found under glacial boulder
beds in the Chanda district. Boulders of Rajasthan rocks have
been transported to the Punjab Salt Range area, probably dropped
there by floating icebergs. Nearer the Himalayas at least two
stages of glaciation are recorded by tillites separated by 500 to 800
m of varved shales. Boulders of the earlier tillite occur in the later
one near Simla. The Talchir tillite has also been recognised in
Assam. In India the centre of ice dispersal lay far to the south.
Much of the evidence for this is lost by erosion or hidden beneath
the Deccan Traps. The ice is supposed to have radiated in a
northerly direction away from the position of the present
equator.

It will be seen from Fig. 10 that the glaciated lands of the Late
Carboniferous period lie on both sides of the equator. This cannot
be explained if the continents had continued to occupy their present
positions. It is explicable only if it is assumed that during the Late
Carboniferous period the continents comprising Gondwanaland

PLATE 23—**Sand dunes partly covering the temple at Talked on the bank of the river Cauvery, Mysore State.** (See Page 143) (*Photo*—C.S. PICHAMUTHU).

PLATE 24—**Scanty bushy vegetation characteristic of arid regions. Rajasthan.** (See Page 146)

PLATE 25—**Shifting sand dunes in the Rajasthan desert.** (See Page 147)

PLATE 26—**Ravines in loess plateau, Punjab.** (See Page 172)

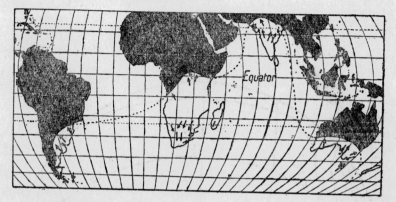

FIG. 10. The dashed line is the northern limit of the Permo-Carboniferous glaciation of Gondwanaland. The continents are in their present positions. The arrows indicate directions of ice-flow (after Holmes).

were aggregated together in some such way as depicted in Fig. 11. Note the position of the equator in this reconstruction.

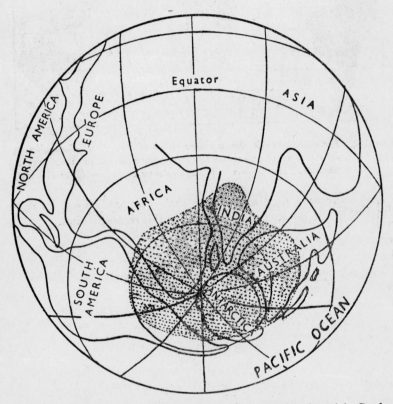

FIG. 11.   Distribution of Permo-Carboniferous glaciation (dotted area) in Gondwanaland.   Note the position of the equator (after Holmes)

CHAPTER XV

LAKES AND SWAMPS

A LAKE IS an inland body of standing water. The water of lakes may be fresh, brackish or salt, but fresh water lakes are far more abundant than the other types. Lakes are among the most widely distributed of all topographic features for they are found at all latitudes and altitudes. Lake Titicaca (area, 8,300 km²) in South America is at an altitude of 4,300 m, while the Dead Sea of Palestine is 435 m below sea level. Lakes vary in depth from a few metres to a maximum of 1,870 m in Lake Baikal of Siberia. India possesses few lakes and none of any considerable size.

Most lakes are parts of river-systems flowing finally into the sea and, therefore, have outlets; but some, like the *salt-lakes*, are situated in areas of *interior drainage* and have no outlet. These salt-lakes accumulate not only the mechanical but also the solution-load of the streams flowing into them.

Two conditions are necessary for the existence of lakes—there should be a basin to hold the water, and there should be a supply of water to fill or partly fill the basin. Lake basins originate in many ways.

Origin of Lakes

Lakes Formed by Crustal Movements: By faulting, a block of the earth's crust may rise or sink relative to an adjacent block, and a trough-like basin forms which gets filled with water. A remarkable example of a trough-fault basin containing a large lake is the Jordan Valley of Palestine with the Dead Sea in its lowest portion. Warping of the earth's crust through differential movement also causes the development of lake basins.

The Rann of Kutch is almost a lake which has originated partly by subsidence resulting from seismic phenomena which accompanied the earthquake of 1815 in that region. The Wular, 100 km² in area, the largest lake in the Kashmir valley which controls the flow of the Jhelum and other rivers, occupies a structural depression. Near Naini Tal in the Kumaun Himalaya, there is a series of lakes which lie along a line formed by faulting.

If part of a river valley is upwarped, it will act as a dam and cause ponding of the water.

Volcanic Lakes: Lake basins may be formed by lava dams; they may occur on the irregular surfaces of a lava flow; or they may be situated in the craters or calderas of extinct volcanoes. The cauldron-like hollow rimmed by blocks of basalt, in which lie the water of Lonar Lake is considered to be an "explosion crater" and, therefore classed as a *crater lake*. It is almost circular in outline, with a diameter of 700 m (*Plate 20*).

Glacial Lake Basins: Deposition of moraines often obstruct the drainage of valleys and produce lakes. Lakes of this type are usually small and are associated with some of the present-day Himalayan glaciers, as in the Chombu glacier in Sikkim. Glaciers may blockade valleys and thus cause ponding of waters. The passage of a glacier transversely across a valley, as in the case of the Chong Kumdan glacier of the Shyok, a tributary of the Indus, produces a temporary lake. Such a lake causes disastrous floods when the ice-dam bursts. A large number of glacial lake basins have been eroded or excavated by the direct action of moving masses of ice.

Lakes Formed by Stream Action: In graded and nearly graded rivers, characteristic of mature and old topography, the shallow basins in abandoned meanders on flood plains form *oxbow lakes*. On many flood-plains small, shallow depressions are left due to irregular deposition of alluvium. After floods or heavy rains, these basins form lakes without natural outlets. As a result of uneven deposition of sediment by the network of distributaries on a delta, some shallow basins are completely surrounded by the deposits and converted into what are known as *delta lakes*. Such lakes are also formed by the enclosing of a hollow between two deltas, as in the case of Kolleru Lake near Eluru in Andhra Pradesh, due to the growth of the Godavari and Krishna deltas.

If two streams on opposite sides of a valley discharge their alluvium on the valley floor, the fans may completely dam the valley forming a lake basin.

Basins are also formed in several other ways. The Chilka Lake of Orissa and the Pulicat Lake of Nellore are examples of lagoons developed by deposits of sand carried up the coast by sea currents in the Bay of Bengal. In these cases, *bars* or *spits* of sand have been deposited across the mouths of small bays or inlets. The backwaters or *kayals* of Kerala State are also due to similar causes.

At the foot of great waterfalls pot-holes are of common occurrence. Such "plunge basins" gradually increase in size and finally become large enough to be called lakes.

Aeolian basins are small and temporary hollows lying among windblown sand heaps and dunes. Examples of such lakes are seen in W. Rajasthan.

Landslides sometimes cause large masses of rocks to fall across stream courses. In some cases permanent lakes are thus formed. The small lakes of Bundelkhand are examples. The Gohna Lake of Garhwal was formed by a huge landslide across a tributary of the Ganga.

Man-made Lakes: Mention may be made here of the artificial lakes and reservoirs which man has created by his engineering skill. He not only makes lakes where there were none before, but he enlarges and strengthens the existing basins.

Salt Lakes: Salt lakes are far less common than fresh water lakes, and exist mainly in arid regions. In a dry climate, a fresh water lake may become a salt lake because the outlet gradually disappears and the mineral matter carried in by streams steadily increases in the water. Great Salt Lake in the United States is one of the best known examples of this type. It is nearly five times as salty as the oceans, that is, it carries about 18 per cent of saline matter in solution.

Some of the lakes of Ladakh and Rupshu in Kashmir, such as Salt Lake, Pangong Lake and Tso Morari, are continually shrinking and becoming more and more saline. These lakes afford clear evidences of desiccation. The Pangong Lake has terraces or beachmarks at various levels, the highest being 40 m above the surface of the present lake. The Tso Morari has terraces at a height of 15 m above the present level of its waters.

Western Rajasthan has many *playa lakes*, that is, interior basins with centripetal drainage. The most important of these is the salt lake of Sambhar which has an area of 24 km² when full during the monsoon at which period the depth of the water is a little above 1 m. During the rest of the year it is dry, the surface being encrusted with a salty silt.

Salt lakes may also be formed by the isolation of arms of the sea by diastrophism or deposition of sediment.

DESTRUCTION OF LAKES

Many causes lead to the destruction of lakes. The streams flowing out of the lakes deepen their outlet and finally drain the basin when its bottom is above the level of the stream-cut valley.

Lake basins are filled in various ways. The sediment carried into lakes by all surface waters especially streams, accumulates on the floor and by gradually filling the basins, finally destroys the lakes. The heads of all Kumaun lakes and of many others such as Loktak Lake in Manipur and Wular Lake in Kashmir, show flat plains which are laid down by the streams which are flowing into them and gradually filling them up.

In humid, temperate-climate regions, lakes are often destroyed by being filled up with vegetable matter. Plants grow in great profusion in the borders of lakes, and as they die, their remains accumulate to form bogs which often encroach from all sides until the lakes are completely filled up.

In regions of present-day glaciation, advancing glaciers often remove morainal dams and destroy lake basins. Lakes formed by ice-dams may be emptied when the ice melts.

In arid regions lakes are destroyed when evaporation exceeds the intake.

SWAMPS

Swamps are basins filled or partially filled with a mixture of water, fresh or decayed vegetation, and soil. *Marsh, bog,* and *morass* come under this category. Swamps are very abundant in humid regions of coastal plains and on flood-plains and deltas where abandoned river channels are filled with vegetation. Wherever the zone of permanent saturation rises above ground level, swamps occur. Conversely, swamps more or less dry up after long periods of dry weather when the water table is lowered below its usual level.

Swamps form in many different ways. Apart from those which occupy glacial basins that have been filled or covered by vegetation, there are many which are found on the seaward margins of coastal plains. These are the result of a slight uplift of the sea-floor, or of the filling of lagoons by silt and vegetation. Mention has already been made of the swamps common on flood-plains and deltas.

The coastal marshes of Bengal and Kerala are swamps which contain a luxuriant growth of the mangrove plant.

Peat which is an early stage in the formation of coal accumulates in bogs. The lignite deposits in Kerala and Madras States must have originated from such peat bogs.

CHAPTER XVI

THE SEA, ITS MOVEMENTS AND WORK

THE SEA AND ITS ORIGIN

ANY VIEW REGARDING the origin of the sea must be related to the origin of the earth itself. According to the Nebular Hypothesis highly heated gas which was part of the original atmosphere condensed to form the waters of the sea. According to the Planetesimal Hypothesis, the masses of matter which gathered together and grew in size were not in a gaseous condition. As the earth thus increased in size, the force of gravity also increased and various gases, including water vapour, were squeezed out to form the atmosphere. Precipitation took place when sufficient water vapour accumulated and the sea began to form. According to this view, the waters of the sea have been forced out of the earth.

Though the exact mode of origin of the sea is not very clear, there is evidence that the sea has been on the earth from very early times. The sedimentary rocks and pillow lavas in Precambrian formations indicate that sea water existed in the oldest periods of earth history.

The terms *sea* and *ocean* in common usage refer to the entire body of salt water which covers a large part of the earth's surface. The oceans are very large deep bodies of sea water occupying basins between continents.

The sea is of great geological importance because of the enormous amount of sediments which are deposited in it. Such marine deposits generally contain the remains of animals and plants. The study of these fossiliferous marine strata has thrown considerable light on the many physical changes through which the earth has passed, and the nature and evolution of life through successive ages. The sea is also an important geological agent which has cut into and modified the bordering land surface. Again, the sea is the source of moisture in the atmosphere, of rain which forms streams, and of snow which constitutes glaciers; all these are active agents which are responsible for considerable weathering and erosion.

The waters of the sea cover nearly three-fourths of the surface of the earth. The average depth of the oceans is about 4 km. The Pacific is the deepest ocean, the greatest depth recorded being 11.04 km in the *Marianas Trench* about 2,000 km east of the Philippine Islands. There are many places in the Pacific Ocean where the water is 6 to 8 km deep. The deepest sounding in the Atlantic Ocean is about 9.5 km off Puerto Rico.

Nearly 78 per cent of the dissolved matter in sea water is common salt. The other principal constituents in solution are chloride and sulphate of magnesia, and the sulphates of lime and potash. These salts have been mainly supplied by rivers which have derived them from the decomposition of the rocks. The principal gases in solution are nitrogen, oxygen, and carbonic acid gas.

The temperature of the surface sea water in the torrid zone is from 24° to 27° C. From this there is a fairly gradual decrease to about — 2°C in the Polar regions. The freezing point of sea water is — 2°C and not 0°C as for fresh water. The variations in the temperature of the surface sea-waters are caused by ocean currents. In the torrid and temperate zones, the temperature is always lower than 4.5° C at depths greater than 1,500 to 2,000 m. The water generally gets colder with increasing depth, even reaching 0.5° C at great depths; this is so even under the equator. In the polar regions the sea from surface to bottom, is at or near the freezing point.

The sea sustains both plants and animals in great abundance. The animals range in size from microscopic forms to giant whales. Lower orders of animals are more common than the higher. The plants are mostly simple forms like seaweeds. In the warmer zones, corals build great reefs in the shallow waters along the sea-shore.

WAVES AND TIDES

Waves are important because of their work of both erosion and deposition. They are produced by the pressure and friction of wind on the sea surface. It should be noted that while the *form* of the wave advances in the direction in which the wind is blowing, there is very little forward movement of the water since the particles of water constituting the wave move in vertical nearly circular orbits. When a wave moves towards the shore on a gently sloping bottom, it becomes shorter and higher and develops an over-steepened crescent-shaped front. Since the motion in the lower part is retarded, the upper part rushes over it forward and downward forming *surf*. The zone in which surf forms is called the *breaker* zone. This forward rush of water carries much sediment with it. After moving up a sloping shore, the water returns seaward as an undercurrent called *undertow*. Wave motion decreases rapidly with depth. Moderately strong waves barely move fine, loose sediment at a depth of 70 m. The maximum depth of water affected by great storm waves is about 200 m.

The *tide* is the periodic rise and fall of the sea produced by the differential attraction of the sun and moon on the ocean. Two high tides are formed at the same time on opposite sides of the earth. Each high tide passes completely around the earth from east to west in 24 hours 52 minutes. Since there are two high tides and two low tides every day, most sea-shores experience high tides approximately every 12 hours 26 minutes, and low tides at a time half way between the high tides. The rising tide is known as *flood tide*. Unlike waves coming into shore, the rise of a flood tide is generally so gradual that it is hardly noticeable.

The importance of tides in modifying shores is due to the raising of the water level and thus making wave action more effective. The currents of a rising tide erode and transport sediments. The depth to which tidal currents scour the ocean floor is much greater than in the case of wave erosion.

The falling tide is known as *ebb tide*. These seaward currents are also important erosive and transporting agents.

In the case of the Hooghly, the influence of the tides is felt as far up the river as the confluence of the Jalangi and the Bhagirathi. At Calcutta the tidal effects are strong and the resultant movements of the waters of the Hooghly actually prevents the formation of a separate delta at the mouth of the river, but there is a continuous deposition especially below Diamond Harbour resulting in the formation of shoals or *sands* such as the James and Mary sands just below the confluence of the Damodar river with the Hooghly.

In funnel shaped estuaries, and in certain large rivers, the concentration of tidal water results in waves called *bores* which rush up bays or rivers with great speed and may raise the water level as much as 20 m. The bore of the Hooghly is noted for its rapid rise and swift flow, the rate of progress up the river being about 30 km an hour, the waves often reaching a height of 1.5 m.

OCEAN CURRENTS

In the equatorial regions of both the Atlantic and Pacific Oceans, the trade winds produce wide westward moving surface currents. On striking the continental coast, each of these currents divides into two, one moving northward and the other southward. Each of these then crosses the ocean eastward and finally turns back into the equatorial belt. Thus in each of these oceans there are two great eddies, one north, and the other south of the equator, with relatively quiet water in the middle. When these wide slow currents approach land, they become narrower and swifter and give rise to so-called *streams*.

Ocean currents are instrumental in producing variations of climate. The hot-weather climate of the coast lands of Malabar and the Konkan is made cooler by the southerly current of water and the north-westerly winds blowing from the Arabian Sea. During the rains, the warmer monsoon currents have the opposite effect. The East African coast is cooled by the current of cold water during the height of the Indian south-west Monsoon. This cold current off the African coast renders the Arabian Sea there too cold for the growth of corals. Off the Malabar Coast, however, the waters of the Arabian Sea are warm and corals flourish, as seen in the atolls of the Laccadive and Maldive archipelagos.

Part of the deflected equatorial current of the Atlantic flowing into the Caribbean Sea and the Gulf of Mexico forms the *Gulf Stream*, one of the swiftest and most important of the ocean currents.

The Hypsographic Curve

The bottom of the sea is generally smoother than the surface of the land, though there are high ridges, plateaus, submarine volcanoes, and valleys. The *continental shelf* is that portion of the continental platform that lies beneath the ocean (Fig. 12). Continental shelves extend to varying distances from the continents, depending upon their slope, until their general surfaces are about 75 fathoms or 135 m below sea level. From the outer limit of the continental shelves the descent to the floor of the ocean basins is generally steep. The slopes, whether gradual or steep, which connect the continental platforms and ocean basins, are known as *continental slopes*. Structurally, the real *ocean basins* must be regarded as commencing, not at the visible shorelines, but at the edge of the continental shelf.

The two Indian seas, the Arabian Sea and the Bay of Bengal which are the northward extensions of the Indian Ocean, originated by the breaking up of the Gondwana continent during the late Cretaceous or early Tertiary times. There is no well-defined continental shelf in these seas, and the 200 m depth line up to which the shelf extends runs roughly parallel to the coast. The width up to 100 m represents the major part of the continental shelf. This zone is about 350 km wide south of Kathiawar, and 220 km wide south of the delta of the Ganga, but, in general, its width ranges from 50 km on the east coast to 100 km on the west coast of the Peninsula.

The maximum width of the continental shelf off the coast of Bombay is about 350 km. The shelf here consists of two distinct terraces separated by a 50-metre bathymetric contour. This terracing is probably caused by the Deccan Trap flows which have given rise to terraced landscape on the adjoining coast. South of this wide submarine platform, the continental shelf narrows down as far as Cape Comorin to between 30 and 100 km. Evidence of submergence, apart from the terraces off the coast of Bombay, is provided by a number of banks on the west continental shelf, chief among them being the Direction, Angria, and Elikalpeni banks. There is a submerged ledge which connects the Laccadive and Maldive Islands to the Suadiva Atoll.

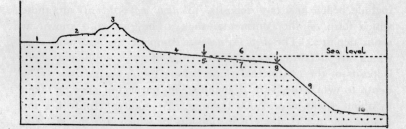

FIG. 12. Hypsographic Curve

1. Interior plain	6. Epicontinental sea
2. Plateau	7. Continental shelf
3. Mountain	8. Edge of continental platform
4. Coastal plain	9. Continental slope
5. Edge of continent	10. Ocean basin.

Except on the north of the Gulf of Mannar and south of the Ganga delta, the width of the east continental shelf is much narrower than the western shelf. North of the Gulf of Mannar, two narrow necks of land project both from India and Ceylon and are connected together by a submerged reef known as Adam's Bridge, which lies only about 4 m below sea level. This is proof of the fact that the sea level rose during the post-glacial period, causing the submergence of the connecting link between India and Ceylon, the latter being part of the same platform as the Indian Peninsula. In contrast to the shelf between India and Ceylon, the shallow continental shelf south of the delta of the Ganga is a plain of sedimentation in which there is a submarine canyon which probably is the submerged course of a former large river of Bengal, the Bhairab. In this part of the Bay of Bengal there is a submerged valley system similar to that in the South China Sea.

Marine Deposits: Normally the sediments on the sea floor become finer and finer as the depth increases, the complete sequence being shingle, sand, silt, and mud. Marine deposits can be classified according to their location on the ocean floor. *Littoral deposits* are formed between the extreme levels of low and high tides, and include beach and bay deposits. *Shallow water deposits* are those which form on the continental shelf. They are also known as *neritic* deposits. The *deep sea deposits* comprise the *muds* and *oozes* which are deposited beyond the edge of the continental shelf. Deposits of the continental slope belong to the *bathyal zone*. The depth to which the bathyal zone extends varies but may be taken as about 4,000 m or 2,000 fathoms. At greater depths lies the *abyssal zone* the characteristic deposits of which are the *red clay*, and the deep-sea oozes composed of pteropods, Globigerina, diatoms, and radiolaria. The temperature of this zone never rises above 4° C.

Marine deposits can also be classified according to the source of their materials. *Terrigenous* deposits are derived from the land by rivers, glaciers, wind, and coast erosion. Such are the shingle, gravel, sand, and mud of the littoral and neritic zones, and the deep-sea muds and sands of the bathyal zone. *Chemical* deposits are precipitated from ocean water with or without the help of organisms. Examples are the oolitic sands, calcareous muds, and evaporites of the shallower zones, and the glauconite and pyrite in the bathyal zone. *Organic* deposits comprise accumulations of calcareous and siliceous shells of marine organisms, such as shell gravels and sands, coral reefs, and coral sands.

Floors of Seas and Oceans

The results of coring, bathyscaphe descents, and a variety of geophysical techniques, have revolutionised our ideas of the floors of seas and oceans. Supersonic waves are now sent from specially equipped ships to the sea bottom, and their reflections are automatically recorded on a chart. These are known as *echograms*, and they give a picture of the profile of the sea floor. The earlier belief that oceanic islands, mainly volcanic peaks and coral islands, rising from great depths were surrounded by vast featureless plains, is now replaced by the knowledge that ocean floors are traversed by great submarine mountain ranges and by numerous rows or clusters of isolated peaks. Some of the higher peaks rise above the level of the sea to form islands, but the vast majority are below sea-level. These are known as *seamounts*; if they have nearly flat tops like truncated cones, they are called *tablemounts* or *guyots*.

Submarine Ridges: As a result of the investigations conducted by the International Indian Ocean Expedition, our knowledge of the Indian Ocean has been greatly enlarged. New major features of the sea floor have been discovered and delineated. A ridge has been found running virtually north and south along the 90°E longitude meridian, and which is continuous from the southeastern part of the Bay of Bengal to nearly 32°S. This ridge which has been called the East Indian Ocean Ridge or "Ninety-degree East Ridge" is about 2,500 m high and 5,750 km long. At 32°S there is a shoal at right angles to this ridge which extends east for about 650 km towards Australia.

The main submarine mountain chain of the Indian Ocean, called the Carlsberg Ridge, starts near the Gulf of Aden, extends south-east, then down the central part of the Indian Ocean, and branches into separate ridges at about 25°S. One part passes south of Africa to join the Mid-Atlantic Ridge, and the other passes south of Australia and joins the East Pacific Ridge. The Carlsberg ridge is broken and displaced to the extent of 400 km at a point south of the Arabian Peninsula, an offset probably related to the John Murray Fault which runs through the Arabian Sea.

The crests of the ridges show considerable topographical relief, which is similar to the other ocean ridges, and is supposed to be caused by the buckling and heat flows from the interior of the earth.

Seamounts have also been discovered in the eastern and western parts of the Indian Ocean.

Submarine Canyons: There are submarine trenches off many coasts which are quite deep and steep-sided just like land canyons. The continental margin is often cut up by such chasms. They begin near the outer edge of the continental shelf and continue down the continental slope for many kilometres till they reach depths of as much as 2,000 m below sea-level. They resemble river valleys in their winding courses, dendritic tributary systems, and V-shaped transverse profiles. Some of them are clearly drowned river valleys.

The exact mode of origin of submarine canyons has given rise to considerable controversy. There is no doubt that they are erosional features, and the fact that they have often been cut through resistant rocks indicates that a powerful agent of erosion must have been at work. Many of these canyons lie at depths at which the ordinary waves and currents of the sea are ineffective. It is now generally believed that they were eroded by *turbidity currents* which are produced by recently deposited marine sediments being stirred up by wave action during violent storms. Such muddy currents would become powerful agents of erosion if they were directed into narrow depressions in the sea-bottom.

Explorations conducted by the International Indian Ocean Expedition in the Bay of Bengal and in the eastern Arabian Sea have revealed abyssal planes related to the sediment discharge from the Ganga-Brahmaputra and Indus rivers, as well as small canyons or turbidity channels. In the Bay of Bengal these channels meander, branch, and rejoin, somewhat like braided streams on land, and appear to run the full length of the planes, with tributaries from either side of the Bay. The tributaries apparently begin on the continental slope in the form of canyons as in the Swatch of No Ground at the head of the Bay of Bengal. Three such depressions, named the Andhra, Mahadevan, and Krishna Canyons, were discovered off the Andhra Pradesh coast. More recently, a series of submarine canyons were noticed off the coast of Madras State between 60 km north-east of Pondicherry and 20 km east of Porto Novo. All these canyons consist of hill-like projections and V-shaped valleys.

ISLANDS AND CORAL REEFS

Sea islands vary in size from small outcrops of rocks to such big ones like Australia. They are formed by diastrophism, wave deposition, wave erosion, volcanic action, and action of organisms.

Islands formed by the action of organisms are chiefly *coral islands*. Corals are tiny animals which thrive in sea-water regions where the temperature does not go below 20° C. The coral polyps secrete calcium carbonate from the sea-water. Chains of islands or long narrow belts consisting of accumulated coral remains are known as *coral reefs*. A coral reef close to the shore is called a *fringing reef*; one situated some distance away from the shore, and somewhat parallel to the shore is a *barrier reef*; and a more or less circular reef enclosing a lagoon is called an *atoll*. *Algae* are minute plants that live in both fresh and salt water. They precipitate calcium carbonate from solution and form deposits of *tufa*.

India possesses a number of islands within its territory both in the Bay of Bengal and the Arabian Sea. The islands in the Bay represent elevated parts of submarine mountains, while those in the Arabian Sea are built of coral.

The group of islands in the Bay of Bengal have an arcuate trend from north-northeast to south-southeast, and lie between 6°45′, and 14°N latitude, and between 92° and 94° E longitude. It is composed of a number of islands, the chief among them being the Andamans and Nicobars. Outside these groups lie the Barren and Narcondam Islands which are extinct volcanoes.

The group of islands in the Arabian Sea comprises the Amindivi, Laccadive, and Minicoy Islands. All these are coral islands and have fringing reefs close to the shore.

CHAPTER XVII

SHORELINES AND COASTAL SCENERY

WAVE EROSION

IN THIS CHAPTER we shall see further aspects of the action of the sea and its results. The energy that works upon and modifies the coast comes largely from the movement of water produced by waves and tides. The physiographical development of shores depends to a large extent on the relief of the coast, and the composition and structure of the rocks outcropping there.

Where the slope of the land is such that the wave breaks, the mass of water dashes powerfully on the coast. This hydraulic pressure dislocates blocks of rocks from cliffs. The air in the many cracks and fissures in the rocks is compressed by breaking waves, which on retreat of the waves, has its pressure suddenly relieved. The expanding air produces an explosive recoil which forces out loose boulders from the face of cliffs. Where strong waves, armed with rock fragments, repeatedly strike a rocky cliff, they become powerful agents of shore destruction.

The height of the waves that break on a shore at high tide marks the upward limit of direct wave action. But by undercutting and caving, the total effect of wave work is considerable.

When waves erode a shore of moderately high land, there develops a steep front facing the sea which is called a *sea cliff* (*Plate 21*). Such a cliff is gradually made to retreat by the erosive action of the waves, and a *wave-cut terrace* is formed which is a shallow water shelf, limited on the land side by a cliff, and with the water increasing in depth seaward to the limit of wave action. A wave-cut terrace is also known as *bench*, *shelf*, *platform*, and *plain*. As the shoreline is cut landward, *stacks*, *caves*, *coves*, *islands*, and other typical erosion remnants are left standing on the wave-cut terrace. *Sea caves* are produced along the bases of cliffs by wave action, especially when the lower parts of cliffs are composed of rocks which are more easily eroded. Unequal wave erosion along a rocky coast often leaves isolated portions of cliffs known as *stacks*. If, along a coast, masses of more easily eroded rocks are separated by harder rocks, the waves cut back the softer rocks to form *sea coves* and *bays* whilst the harder and more massive rocks project into the sea to form *headlands*.

A wave-cut terrace by uplift of land becomes a *plain of marine erosion*. In some respects this resembles a stream-developed peneplain, since the surface of such a terrace cuts across all kinds of rocks irrespective of their composition and structure. The surface is usually smoother but the erosion remnants left by the waves are steeper-sided than those on a peneplain formed by streams. A fine example of a long plain of marine erosion with steep sided isolated masses (former islands) rising above its surface occurs on the eastern side of India.

Beaches are the deposits of loose material within the reach of the waves along the shore. They are well developed on gently sloping coastal plains. Where the wave-cut terraces are narrow, the undertow and littoral currents carry the debris eroded from the land out into deep water, where it is deposited. The beaches are thus built gradually away from the coastline, thus extending the land seaward. Some beaches are like ridges with a crest and a steeper slope towards the land than the sea. Others are broad sheets of sediments spread by waves and currents over the shore. They may be composed of sand, gravel, or rounded pebbles.

The material which is carried back into the sea by undertow often accumulates in an offshore zone as a long *barrier beach* or *barrier bars*, or a series of *barrier islands*, parallel to the general coastline. The shallow water of the area between the barrier and the shore is called a *lagoon* or *sound*.

When a sediment-laden shore current comes to a cove or narrow embayment on the coast, it keeps its course without following the indentations of the shore. Since the littoral current moves into deeper and calmer water its velocity is retarded and the load it is carrying is deposited, and a *spit* is formed. The normal form of a spit is slightly concave seaward. When the spit grows to a stage when it nearly or completely closes the embayment, it is called a bar.

Wave-built terraces are formed where the sea-cliff and wave-cut terrace are both being eroded by wave action, and the loosened material is gradually shifted and deposited in deeper water at the seaward edge of the wave-cut terrace. Wave-cut and wave-built terraces together constitute the continental shelf.

Shorelines: The zone between the low tide mark and the highest wave mark is the *shore*. The line that separates land and water is the *shoreline*. In both cases it is a migrating line.

Shorelines are formed in many different ways, and they can be divided into four principal types: (i) shorelines of submergence, (ii) shorelines of emergence, (iii) neutral shorelines, and (iv) compound shorelines.

(i) *Shorelines of Submergence:* Nearly all the present marine shorelines show effects of fairly recent submergence. This is because the four advances and retreats of the Pleistocene glaciers resulted in considerable changes in sea level. At the maximum height of any glaciation the sea level was at least 300 m below its present position. Due to the melting of the ice during the last retreat of glaciation, the water rose and submerged areas which were land. It is estimated that if all the present glaciers were to melt, the sea would rise about 60 to 70 m above its present level. Another cause of submergence is *subsidence* of the land.

When a region of hills and valleys is submerged under the sea, a very irregular and deeply indented shoreline results giving rise to bays, estuaries, gulfs, fiords, and straits, separated by headlands, peninsulas, and off-shore islands. When sea water enters the valleys *estuaries* are formed; they are relatively shallow. In glaciated regions of high relief, the valleys are cut well below sea level, and when the ice melts, sea water enters the valleys forming *fiords*. Fiords are long narrow arms of the sea with steep smooth sides and great depth.

The coastline of the Andaman Islands is highly indented. The branching fiords of the Andamans and Nicobars are the consequence of submergence of these islands.

One of the most remarkable examples of a submerged land surface with drowned valleys that can still be recognized on the sea floor, is that which formerly connected Malaya with the islands of Sumatra, Java and Borneo (Fig. 13). The curtailed and dismembered present-day valleys can be traced down to depths of about 100 m

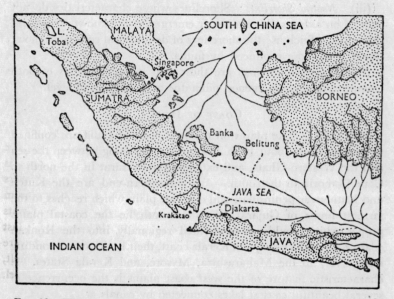

FIG. 13. The drowned river systems of the south-east Asia, still identifiable across the shallow parts of the Gova and South China Seas (after Umbgrove)

in the South China and Java seas where they join to form a few river systems.

(ii) *Shorelines of Emergence:* Shorelines of emergence are formed by tectonic uplift of the land. The following are some of the characteristics of emerged shorelines—(1) Uplifted wave-cut plains on which there may be stacks, and on the landward edge, sea cliffs and caves; (2) Wave-formed terraces; (3) Raised beaches which are well above the present sea level; and (4) Straight shorelines, which result by the recent uplift of the flat portion of a continental shelf.

There is a raised sea beach on the west or seaward side of Bombay Island, while a submerged forest occurs on the east or harbour side. This indicates movement of the land either in opposite directions along a North-South fault line, or perhaps a tilting of the island.

(iii) *Neutral Shorelines*: Shorelines whose characteristics do not depend on either submergence or emergence, are known as neutral shorelines. Such are the shorelines of deltas, coral reefs, volcanoes, dunes, and those produced by faults.

(iv) *Compound shorelines* are those that exhibit features of both emergence and submergence, often due to oscillations of level.

COAST OF INDIA

West Coast: The plains on the west coast of India are confined to a narrow belt about 10 to 25 km wide stretching between the sea and the Western Ghats, and extending from Surat in the north to Cape Comorin in the south. At the northern end are the Kutch and Kathiawar peninsulas, and one vast plain which reaches to the farthest limits of Gujarat. Further south lie the coastal plains proper which could be subdivided regionally into the Konkan coast, Karnataka coast, and Kerala coast, their limits corresponding respectively to the Maharashtra, Mysore, and Kerala States. A characteristic feature of the west coast plains is the occurrence of several beautiful coastal lakes connected by canals.

The *Kutch peninsula* was once an island surrounded by seas and lagoons until the Great and Little Rann of Kutch got silted up. Lack of rainfall in this region has given rise to arid and semi-arid landscape, and hence, coastal sand dunes, sandy plains, and bare rocky hills are the characteristic physiographic features of the Kutch peninsula. The Great Rann is a broad plain formed of dark silt with salt encrustation, the plain rising only a few metres above the sea level; in some places it is actually below sea level. Patches of high ground, some rocky and some sandy covered with grass, rise like islands above the level of the barren plains. The Rann gets flooded every year partly by river water and partly by the rise of the sea.

The *Kathiawar peninsula* lies to the south of Kutch.   Two Ranns, the Little Rann of Kutch and the Rann of Cambay, along with the Nal lake, nearly encircle the peninsula on the east and northeast. There is a central tableland from which all the rivers of this peninsula arise and radiate outwards.   In the southern part there are some high hills (Mt. Girnar, 1,117 m).   The Gir Range with its dense forests is famous as the home of the Indian lion.   Many of the hills in this region are volcanic in origin and are of the cuesta type, the seaward slope being steeper than the inland side.

The *Gujarat plains* lie to the east of Kathiawar and stretch towards the interior highlands.   Wind-blown loess covers the greater part of the country nearer the coast, which by weathering has given rise to a semi-arid type of landscape.

The *Konkan coast* is characterised by cliffs of basaltic trap rocks, and stretches from north of Goa to Daman, a distance of 500 km. There are submerged forests near the city of Bombay, as well as raised terraces formed of coral reefs or of loosely cemented fragmentary shell limestone rocks.   South of Bombay city, the rocky coast has a series of small bays and coves lying between jutting headlands, and containing beautiful beaches formed of bright white sands.

The *Karnataka coast* has several rocky cliffs.   The chief river in this region is the Sharavathi which, before entering the plains, plunges down a cliff 275 m high at the Gersoppa or Jog falls.   The plains are nowhere more than 24 km wide and are often only 8 km.

The *Kerala plains* are comparatively much wider and less hilly. A number of lakes or backwaters (*kayals*) lies along the coast, the largest of which is the Vembanad kayal which stretches for more than 80 km.

East Coast: The Madras and Andhra Pradesh coast extends from Cape Comorin northwards to the Krishna and Godavari deltas for 1,100 km with an average width of 120 km.   Further north, the hills almost approach the sea.   The coastal plains again widen north of Berhampur and extend to the Chilka lake, the Mahanadi delta, and the Balasore coastal plain, where they merge into the deltaic plains of the Ganga.

In the *Madras coast*, the Cauvery delta is the most important physiographic feature.

The *Andhra plains* stretch from near Berhampur to the Pulicat lake, 50 km north of Madras city. Two of the biggest rivers of the Deccan, the Krishna and the Godavari, flow in this region and form deltas. Between the two deltas is the Kolleru lake which affords evidence of the coastal plain towards the sea. The Krishna after passing through a deep gorge cut in khondalite rocks enters the coastal plains at Vijayawada and flows for 90 km before it reaches the sea. The Godavari emerges on the plains from a gorge at Polavaram and soon divides into two distributaries between which the main delta lies.

The *Orissa plains* include the Mahanadi delta with Cuttack at its head. The seaward margin of this delta is straighter than that of the Ganga delta and is fringed with sand dunes. The most important physiographic feature south of the Mahanadi delta is the Chilka lake which is a pear-shaped expanse of water, 70 km long. Its origin is due to the formation of a bar at the mouth of the bay. Two streams drain into the lake which contains a number of rocky islands and is bordered by hills on the south and west.

CHAPTER XVIII

WIND, ITS CIRCULATION AND WORK

CAUSE OF WINDS

THOUGH less effective than running water, wind is an important agent of erosion and transportation of rock material. Wind may be defined as air in motion nearly parallel to the earth's surface. There are many types of winds, such as trade winds and westerlies, monsoon winds, winds associated with cyclones and anticyclones, hurricanes, typhoons and tornadoes, mountain and valley breezes, land and sea breezes, and so on. The chief cause of wind is the unequal heating of the atmosphere by the sun which results in difference in barometric pressure between places. An illustration of this is land and sea breezes. During a hot day in summer, the land and the air over it get more heated than the adjoining sea and the air over it. Consequently, the air rises over the land, the air pressure becomes less, and the cooler heavier air moves in from over the sea, creating a *sea breeze*. The conditions are reversed during the night, the wind blows from land to sea, and this is known as a *land breeze*.

TRADE WINDS

Air is cold over the polar regions and hot over the equatorial belt and so, if the earth did not rotate, heated air would rise at the equator and blow towards the poles where, after becoming cold and heavy, it would come down and return towards the equator. The earth's rotation, however, deflects the course of these winds. The high altitude winds that blow from the equator to the poles are deflected to the east, and the return winds which complete the convection current near the ground are deflected to the west, and hence, become the "easterlies". There are the NE and SE *trade winds* which blow across a broad belt on either side of the equator,

and less regularly, in the polar regions. Separating the polar
easterlies from the tropical trade winds, there is a belt of irregular
"westerlies," where the weather is very disturbed and variable.

The heated air ascending from the equatorial "doldrums" turns
towards the poles at a height of about 10 to 13 km and passes into
latitudes which are narrower than the equator. A few degrees N
or S of Latitude 30° (which is 13 per cent shorter than the equator),
the crowding of the air raises the pressure and so the air moves
downwards. These are the high pressure sub-tropical calm belts
known as the "Horse Latitudes". The descending air is divided
into the trade winds that blow towards the equator and the dis-
orderly westerlies that spiral towards the poles. The latter meet
the cold surface winds already blowing from the poles and this
confrontation makes the weather very disturbed and variable.

In the northern hemisphere the cold polar air advances far to the
south in winter and withdraws to the north in the summer. Similarly, in the southern hemisphere, there is a winter advance to the
north and a summer retreat to the south. The spread of this *polar
front* is much wider over land than over the oceans, since the oceans
have a moderating influence because of the relative slowness with
which water gains or loses heat.

CYCLONES AND ANTICYCLONES

In each hemisphere three convection currents are formed. The
high altitude westerlies are concentrated between the tropics and
the poles; they do not, however, blow straight towards the poles
but swing far to the north and south. These swirls result in atmospheric eddies which are known as *cyclones* and *anticyclones*.

A condition of low atmospheric pressure in which the isobars
(lines joining places along which the sea-level air-pressure is the
same) form closed curves is a *depression* or *cyclone*. An *anticyclone* is
a condition of high atmospheric pressure in which the isobars form
closed curves. Wind always blows from a place where the pressure
is high to one where it is lower, and the force of such a wind depends
upon the difference in pressure between the two places, *i.e.* upon
the barometric gradient. The wind moves in an anticlockwise

spiral motion in a cyclone in the northern hemisphere. There is an upward current of air above the central low-pressure area and consequently the air from the surrounding region flows in to take its place. The ascending air in the middle of a cyclone expands as its pressure decreases. The expansion is accompanied by cooling which causes condensation of its moisture in the form of rain.

In anticyclones in the northern hemisphere, the air movements take the form of right-handed outward moving spirals, and hence, the winds move in a clockwise manner. The winds are generally stronger in cyclones than in anticyclones.

Almost all cyclonic storms in the Bay of Bengal originate or are produced in the Bay itself and move north-westwards into Bengal, Bihar, and Orissa. They occasionally travel across the Peninsula to the Arabian Sea.

When tropical oceanic areas become highly heated, streams of air rapidly rise and create the terribly devastating winds known as *hurricanes* (from a Caribbean word meaning 'spirit of evil'). These are prevalent in the Atlantic Ocean and its big Mexican, Caribbean, and Mediterranean embayments. *Typhoons* are similar violent whirlwinds which are common in the west Pacific Ocean, especially between Australia and Japan. South winds in the Indian Ocean are referred to as *tropical cyclones*. The ordinary cyclones in temperate regions are usually 1,500 km or more across, but hurricanes and typhoons are only 350 or 450 km in diameter, and so the pressure gradient is quite steep from the outer rim where the pressure is highest to the "eye" in the middle where the pressure is lowest. The hot moist winds whirling upwards reach speeds of 150 to 200 km or even 300 km per hour, and as the rising air expands and cools the water vapour condenses into very heavy stormy rainfall.

The *tornado* which often begins as an off-shoot of a severe hurricane, is a narrow column of rapidly rotating air rarely 2 km across and generally much less. The rotation of the wind is so violent that a tornado causes great material damage. It is accompanied by torrential rain.

Monsoons

The name *monsoon* is derived from a Malay word meaning a "season". The primary cause for the arrival and withdrawal of the monsoon is the variation of the quantity of the sun's heat received by the land surface of India according as the sun is in north or south declination, *i.e.*, north or south of the celestial equator. The monsoon winds which change with the season are like the alternating land and sea breezes of night and day, due to the unequal warming of land and sea, and blow, in general, from cooler to warmer regions.

During the hot weather, as a consequence of the inclination of the earth's axis, the heat equator (the line joining the hottest places on successive meridians—this is not, however, an isotherm) moves northwards, and the land masses of Central Asia receive a greater amount of heat from the sun than the waters of the Indian and Pacific Oceans near the equator. Since even an equal amount of heat is sufficient to raise the temperature of the land higher than that of the sea, it is obvious why the summer of Central Asia becomes very hot. The heated air rises and cooler air from the south and east flows towards the area of low barometric pressure thus produced.

The North-East Trade Winds, which otherwise would flow over the Indian Ocean north of the equator, are subordinated by this powerful wind northwards. The South-East Trade Winds, on the other hand, are drawn across the equator and deflected to the right to blow over India from May to September as the South-West Monsoon. Thus the South-West monsoon is a dry wind when it blows across the Arabian Sea, but where it is forced up into the upper air as when it meets the Western Ghats or the Himalayas, it is cooled by expansion and the moisture comes down as heavy rain. This is also the reason why the rainfall on the southern slopes of the eastern Himalayas in the monsoon from the Bay of Bengal is heavier than that on the central Himalayas. The rainfall at Cherrapunji, on the southern edge of the Shillong plateau and nearer the Bay of Bengal, is the heaviest known, for the average annual rainfall is 1,160 cm.

During the cold weather the heat equator moves southward and the conditions are reversed. Northern Australia now becomes a centre of high temperature and low pressure, while Central Asia is a region of excessive cold and high pressure. Consequently, the winter monsoon over India blows from the northeast.

GEOLOGICAL ACTION OF WIND

Winds not only erode, transport, and deposit rock materials, but also stir up waves and shore currents which in turn become powerful agents of gradation. The geological action of wind, just as in the case of its companions, running water and glaciers, is twofold, (i) erosion and (ii) deposition. Wind *erosion* is mainly of two types— *deflation* and *corrasion*. The difference between these two modes of removal and transportation of material is that deflation is done without the aid of tools whereas corrasion requires the assistance of grinding materials.

Wind is most active as an agent of *deflation*. Dust and sand, which are loosened particles of rock, are transported from one place to another, especially in regions where there is little or no vegetation. Deflation is particularly active on ploughed fields, alluvial plains and similar regions, where from time to time, loose, fine-grained soil and silt are exposed. Such movements are specially in evidence in desert country where winds are more continuous and stronger, and hence, erosion is much greater. Large quantities of dust are thrown into the atmosphere by the explosive eruptions of volcanoes and these are transported for great distances by wind.

The enormous transporting power of strong winds over deserts is illustrated by sand storms, when many cubic kilometres of dust and sand-laden air travel over long distances across the country. Such dust storms are common in India but particularly troublesome at times in northern India where they are known as *loo*. Many of these dust storms are due to convection currents set up in dry air, and originate in arid areas due to the rarefaction of the air by continued heating of the ground surface. These storms travel at 70 to 100 km an hour and fill the whole atmosphere with dust.

Wind by itself has little or no power to abrade or *corrade* solid rocks. But it is very powerful when supplied with tools, that is, when it has rock fragments with which to work. When grains of sand are driven by strong winds against hard rocks, the latter are worn and often polished. Where such ledges of rocks show local variations in composition, they are often etched into irregular, and often fantastic, forms. The rapid corrasion effected by winds under favourable conditions is illustrated by plate glass windows of lighthouses being worn to opaqueness during a single severe wind storm.

The greatest erosive power of wind-blown sand is close to the ground because of the presence of the larger and heavier fragments which are carried at that level by the wind. Hence, undercutting is a marked feature of wind abrasion (*Plate 22*).

By continued attrition due to the friction of impact and rolling, the sand grains themselves are gradually worn down and rounded. Wind is more effective than water in rounding sand grains. Some of the *millet seed sands* of the desert are almost perfect spheres with a frosted surface like that of ground glass.

Wind Transportation: Wind moves dust and sand in several ways. The fine, light materials are picked up, suspended in the air, and carried away, whereas the heavy or large sand grains are rolled along the surface of the ground. The occurrence of dust or sand storms gives an idea of the enormous amount of material eroded and transported by wind.

Wind Deposition: Material transported by wind is finally deposited due to reduction in its velocity. *Loess* is an accumulation of wind-borne dust and silt, washed down from the air by rain, and held together by the growth of grass. It is usually a fine-grained, unstratified, yellow to brown loam which, though slightly consolidated, is capable of standing in the form of high, steep cliffs after erosion. It generally forms very thick deposits.

Dunes: Hills of wind-blown sands are called *dunes* (*Plate 25*). Although they are abundant in desert regions, they are not confined to deserts or even to semi-arid regions. They are formed wherever there is dry sand and where the winds are of sufficient strength to move the sand. They are, therefore, found on and near the sandy shores of lakes or oceans where the wind blows towards the land; and on and near river flood plains.

If wind, blowing sand along just above the ground, meets an irregularity of the surface or some obstacle such as a bush or boulder, the velocity of the wind is checked and sand is deposited on the leeward side of the obstruction. The initial deposit of sand then forms a further obstruction resulting in more sand being deposited; this process continues and a dune is formed. Dunes vary in size from a few metres to as much as 175 m in height, and correspondingly in length. Where the direction of the wind remains fairly constant, a gentle slope develops on the windward side and a steep slope on the leeside; the smaller dunes are often somewhat crescent shaped because the wind drives the sand both over and around the dune. This type is known as a *barchan*. Where the winds are variable in direction, the dunes are more irregular in shape. A dune is usually crudely stratified and coarsely cross bedded. Beautifully regular ripple marks are generally formed on the surfaces of sand dunes.

Where they are not held in place by vegetation, dunes almost always migrate in the direction of the prevailing wind. This is caused by the wind blowing the sand grains up the gentle windward side of the dune and letting them fall down on the steeper leeward side. Most dunes migrate at rates of from a few metres to more than 30 m per year. Where the sand is very dry and the wind is very strong, migration is rapid. Villages and cities have sometimes been buried.

Sand dunes are common in western India in the Rajasthan desert, and in a few coastal tracts. The temple at Talkad on the banks of the Cauvery in Mysore State is in constant danger of being buried under advancing sand dunes (*Plate 23*).

Wind-blown material does not always accumulate in the form of dunes and ridges. Wind action often levels large areas by removing loose materials from higher lands and depositing them in intervening depressions, or piling them up against the base of mountains. This is characteristically seen in the Sahara Desert where some large areas of bed-rock are kept free from sand by wind erosion, and the sand is piled against the mountain bases, and even up the slopes to heights of 300 to 600 m.

CHAPTER XIX

DESERTS AND THEIR TOPOGRAPHY

DISTRIBUTION OF DESERTS

ARID DESERTS and sub-arid deserts cover nearly one-third of the land surface of the earth. An arid desert is characterised by a lack of moisture. Either there may be very little initial moisture, or the moisture that does occur is rapidly evaporated by very high temperatures.

The deserts of the low and middle latitudes fall into two general groups — the topographical deserts and tropical deserts. The *topographical deserts* have deficiency of rainfall either because they are situated far away from oceans, in the middle of continents, or what is more common, because the rain-bearing winds are intercepted by high mountains which surround them. *Tropical deserts* are found in zones which range between 5 to 30 degrees north and south of the equator. These are the trade-wind belts. In the northern hemisphere belt the trade-winds blow from the north-east to the south-west, while in the southern hemisphere belt they blow from the south-east towards the north-west. They blow, therefore, from relatively cooler to relatively warmer regions. So long as their course is over the sea or over low-lying land, the trade-winds are dry. But, when they strike mountains they rise up and are chilled by expansion. The abundant moisture they contain is precipitated as rain. This is why the eastern slopes of high lands in the trade-wind belts have a heavy rainfall whereas the low-lying lands and the *western slopes* of elevated regions are dry and often exhibit the "desert" type of climate. This is the reason why more than half of the land lying in the trade-wind belts consists of dry deserts. They include the Sahara Desert of North Africa, the Arabian Desert of the Middle East, the Desert of Australia, the Kalahari

Desert of South Africa, the Sonora Desert of north-western Mexico, Southern Arizona, and California, the Atacama Desert of Peru and Chile, and the deserts of Afghanistan, Baluchistan and north-western India.

CLIMATE

Rainfall in the deserts is both scanty and irregular. Most deserts receive, on an average, only 25 to 35 cm of rainfall a year, and some receive less. Over much of the Sahara desert, for example, the mean annual rainfall is usually less than 12 cm. Some parched areas go for years without a single drop of rain.

Temperatures in the desert vary from one extreme to the other in just a few hours. The air is rapidly heated during the day and cools suddenly at night, particularly in the tropical deserts in both hemispheres, where winter and summer temperatures are very much alike. Winter temperatures are not quite so high as in summer — the night temperature occasionally drops below freezing — but during the day the temperature quickly rises even to 30°C.

To add to the unpleasantness of the desert climate, violent winds often blow across the dry earth. Because of lack of vegetation, large clouds of dust rise to great heights above the ground and drive particles of sand along the surface of the land.

WEATHERING AND SOILS

Both chemical and mechanical weathering is extremely slow in the desert because of the lack of moisture. Mechanical weathering predominates resulting in unaltered rock and mineral fragments. Some mechanical weathering is merely the result of gravity as when the shattered rock material falls from a cliff. Wind-driven sand causes some amount of mechanical weathering. The great variations in temperature characteristic of deserts cause rock materials to expand and contract, thus producing some mechanical weathering.

Residual soil is rarely formed, because the lack of protective vegetation permits the winds to blow it away. Even so, soils may develop sometimes in local areas, but they lack the humus of the soils in moister climates, and they contain concentrations of such soluble substances as calcite, gypsum and even halite because there is not enough water to dissolve them.

WATER

Although rainfall is extremely sparse in desert areas, there is still enough water to act as an agent of erosion, transportation, and deposition.

Very few streams flowing through deserts ever reach the sea. Most desert stream beds are mostly dry, and flow only when there is an occasional flood. Even then the flow is only for a short period for the water either evaporates rapidly or vanishes into the highly permeable sand. Sometimes, broad desert plains slope toward central basins, called *playas*, where surface waters collect from time to time. Such *playa lakes*, however, usually dry up in a short time, or exist as shallow salty lakes, of which the Great Salt Lake in U.S.A. is a good example.

Because of the low rainfall, ground-water supplies are poor in desert areas. Even the water that does fall, evaporates before it can reach underground reservoirs. The little water that may sink to the zone of aeration is used by desert plants, but most of it is drawn back to the surface by evaporation and enters the atmosphere.

DESERT TOPOGRAPHY

Because of deficiency in rainfall there is only a thinly scattered vegetative cover (*Plate 24*). Bare slopes or those sparsely covered with arid types of plants and shrubs offer little obstruction to mechanical weathering and to erosion. Wind which blows up slopes quite as much as down slopes, searches out and removes dust wherever it is found. All these combine to produce a landscape distinctive of deserts. The vistas appear infinite because there are no trees to obstruct the vision to the distant horizon and up into the cloudless skies. Most of the country consists of open plains over which are found wind-swept slopes of bare rock or rubble, flat salt-encrusted playas, and slowly moving sand dunes (*Plate 25*). There are occasional mountains and steep-walled canyons. The nature of the bedrock has a much more striking effect on the appearance of the landscape than it does in humid areas, where because of the abundance of water, vegetation and soils cover the slopes and hide the irregularities in the bedrock. In the desert, therefore, the geological structure of the earth's crust is very clearly seen.

In a humid climate, the end product of erosion is generally a gently rolling plain called a peneplain. But in arid and semi-arid climates, the steep faces of an uplifted mountain or high plateau are attacked by agents of erosion and worn backward. As a result, slopes are carved on the bedrock, which grade downward towards desert streams or basins. These surfaces of erosion are known as *pediments*. With time, the mountain mass is destroyed or reduced to a low dome with just a few projections of resistant rock rising above the surface. Whereas the peneplain does not appear until old age in a humid climate, the pediment is present from the beginning of the arid cycle. With the progress of erosion, the pediments increase in area and the mountain or plateau zones decrease. The slope of the scarp at the head of the pediment or the slope of the pediment itself do not become appreciably gentler from the beginning of the cycle to the end, whereas the slopes developed in more humid climates become less steep with the passage of time.

ARID REGIONS OF INDIA

The dry plains of Punjab extend southwards and merge gradually into the arid plains of Rajasthan. This arid region is bounded on the east by the Aravalli range. The general elevation of this country varies between 150 and 300 m. The landscape evolution of this desert region is different from the rest of the Indo-Gangetic plain, because wind has taken an upper hand over running water in landscape evolution. It is a region of deficient rainfall and moving sands. The dry beds of former rivers indicate the gradual desiccation of this region. The Luni (or Salt River) is the only flowing river in these arid plains, and even this carries a mere trickle of water in years of deficient rainfall.

The ground-water in the greater part of this arid land is impregnated with salt. There are a number of salt lakes in this arid region of which the Sambhar is the largest. It lies 60 km west of Jaipur town, and covers 300 km^2 during the rainy season. In the dry months its surface is encrusted with bright white saline soils. Salt is manufactured from the brine of this lake.

A 100 km wide strip along the western border of Rajasthan between the parallels of 26° and 29° N includes more than three-fourths of the sandy desert. Here the annual rainfall is very low— about 15 cm per year. There are numerous sand dunes which, west of Shahgarh, run in chains of a complex pattern, the longitudinal type predominating. South of 26° N latitude, the dunes continue but are generally of the barchan or transverse type. In the Barmer region the barchans are 5 m to 100 m high.

North of Jaisalmer there are a number of playa lakes called Ranns which occur in basins rimmed by low scarps. These lakes, though fed by centripetal drainage, remain dry for the greater part of the year.

A belt of steppe country stretches westwards from the foot of the Aravalli range and merges gradually into the desert region. There are fewer dunes in this region which is drained by numerous short streams. The highest group of hills in Western Rajasthan occurs here. Parts of the hilly tract are buried under sand, but it represents fluvial landscape carved out by earlier powerful rivers, modified by later aeolian erosion.

The Thar desert of Rajasthan to the south of the Himalayan chain and the vast Taklamakan desert to the north form part of the large desert belt of Central Asia which is continuous with the Sahara. The aridity of this region appears to have been caused only in very recent times, since all along this vast extent there are remains of flourishing human settlements, with forests and other evidences of humid climate. The continental desiccation has been caused by the deflection of moisture bearing winds from the

Indian Ocean with consequent disruption of the drainage pattern of the country.

Because of the meteorological influence of the Himalayas on the atmospheric circulation, the Thar area of Rajasthan has not felt the full impact of this desiccation. On account of its altitude and its location directly in the path of the monsoons, the Himalayan mountain system precipitates much of their moisture either as rain or snow, which feed a number of rivers flowing down to the southern plains. In this way, the Himalayas have protected this area from the desiccation which has spread over Central Asia. On the other hand, the interception by the Himalayan chain of the monsoon wind circulation from the ocean, has gradually desiccated parts of Tibet and the Tarim basin to its northwest, which are some of the most desolate regions of the earth today because the river systems have withered away in the growing volume of sands.

CHAPTER XX

CLIMATE AND CLIMATIC TYPES

WEATHER AND CLIMATE

Weather is the condition of the atmosphere at any moment with regard to air temperature, barometric pressure, wind velocity, humidity, clouds, and precipitation. The *climate* of a place may be defined as the average condition of the weather at that place, and depends chiefly on the following factors: (1) latitude, (2) elevation, (3) distance from the sea, (4) ocean currents, (5) prevailing winds, and (6) land relief, especially the position and direction of mountain ranges.

The latitude of a place determines its seasons and the duration of daylight at different periods of the year. The difference in length between the longest and the shortest day increases with latitude. Hence, other things being equal, the higher the latitude of a place, the greater will be the difference there between summer and winter.

As the height above sea-level increases, the average temperature decreases at the rate of about 1°C for every 155 m of vertical height. This is known as the lapse rate of temperature in the troposphere. This happens because air is only very slightly heated by the direct rays of the sun, and gets nearly all its heat by conduction from the ground.

The proximity of a place to the sea does not affect much the average temperature for a year, but has a great equalising effect, making winters warmer and summers cooler than they are in the interiors of continents. The sea does not vary in temperature nearly so much as the land does, owing partly to its free circulation and partly to its high specific heat (*i.e.* to raise the temperature of a given weight of water one degree requires much more than is needed to raise by one degree the temperature of an equal weight of any solid material). This is the reason why places far from the sea, or those shut off from the sea by high mountains, have extreme or *continental climates*, with a great difference of temperature between summer and winter; whereas, small islands and the coasts of continents have *insular* or *oceanic* climates with a much smaller range of temperature.

Ocean currents act only indirectly on land climates by altering the temperature of the air which blows over them. Prevailing winds exercise a very important influence both on temperature and rainfall.

Mountain ranges produce very important differences of climate. When they are situated near the coast they act as barriers preventing the moderating influence of the sea from spreading inland. The influence of mountains on rainfall commences a long distance from their actual slopes, but becomes greater as these are approached. Mountains also affect the temperatures of places by shielding them from cold or warm winds.

CLIMATIC FACTORS

Temperature is one of the most important factors of climate. It is recorded by what is known as a *thermometer*. Two kinds of thermometer scales are in common use. One is known as the Centigrade scale, and the other as the Fahrenheit scale. The *Freezing Point*, that is the temperature at which water freezes into ice, is marked 0° on a Centigrade thermometer, and 32° on a Fahrenheit thermometer. The *Boiling Point*, that is the temperature at which water begins to boil, is marked 100° on the Centigrade thermometer and 212° on the Fahrenheit thermometer. In India the Centigrade scale is adopted.

In order to compare the temperature conditions between different periods in the same place or between different places, it is necessary to prepare isothermal maps. On such a map, lines are drawn connecting those places which have the same temperature (reduced to sea-level by allowing for the effect of altitude upon temperature) at any given time, in order to get an idea of the distribution of temperature of air at the earth's surface at the time. Such lines are known as *isotherms*. Isothermal maps display in a striking manner the modification of temperature caused by such circumstances as varying season, latitude, proximity to the ocean, direction of prevailing winds, etc. It should, however, be remembered that isothermal charts are constructed from readings of temperature *reduced to sea-level*; so they do not show local differences of temperature due to elevation. This will have to be calculated by subtracting from the temperature indicated by the isotherms, 1°C for every 155 m of elevation. The most useful isothermal maps are those for January and for July, the two months which as a rule, exhibit the greatest extremes of temperature.

Of all the forms of condensed moisture the most important, because it is the commonest and most abundant, is rain. The amount of rain which falls in a place is referred to as the *rainfall* of that place. This has an influence on the climate. It is usual to add the amounts of rainfall for several successive years together and divide by the number of years, thus obtaining the average for the years taken; such a result is known as the *mean annual rainfall* of the place.

The various gases which make up the atmosphere have a very considerable weight that exerts a force upon the surface of the earth which is known as *air pressure*. This is measured by a *barometer* (Greek *baros*=weight).

The pressure of the air varies in the same place because an increase of temperature produces a diminution in the density of the atmosphere, and consequently a diminution of pressure. Again, since water vapour is lighter than air, if there is a large amount of water vapour present in the atmosphere at a place, the air is made lighter, bulk for bulk, resulting in diminution of pressure.

Other circumstances remaining the same, an increase of temperature is accompanied by a fall of pressure, *i.e.*, where the thermometer is high the barometer is low. Likewise, an increase of the amount of water vapour in the air will result in a lower barometer reading. In order to map the pressure conditions over an area, lines are drawn connecting all place which have the same barometer reading at any given time, after these readings have been reduced to 0°C and mean sea level (M.S.L.). Lines so obtained are called "equal pressure lines" or *isobars*.

The air moves from places where the pressure is high towards places where the pressure is low. These movements constitute winds. The winds are *permanent* if the difference of pressure causing them continues throughout the year; they are *periodic* if the pressure differences arise only at definite intervals. *Variable* winds result from any local disturbances of pressure. Variations in pressure are the results of changes in temperature and of the increase or decrease of the amount of water vapour held in the air. These alterations are, therefore, to be regarded as the primary causes of the various types of winds which in their turn, have a control on the characteristics of climates.

WEATHER CHARTS

In order to ascertain the conditions on which the various types of weather depend, and to form forecasts of the weather, atmospheric changes which occur at different observing stations are recorded on weather charts. The corrected barometer readings received daily from different stations are marked upon the map at the points representing the positions of those stations. Isobars are then drawn joining those places where the pressure is the same. Pressures are stated in units called *millibars* (mb), 1,000 mb corresponding to a barometer height of 75 cm. When isobars are close together, they represent a considerable difference of pressure in a short distance and, therefore, the wind is strong. The difference of pressure between two places, divided by the distance between them, is known as the *barometric gradient*; the force and velocity of the wind are directly proportional to this gradient.

CLASSIFICATION OF CLIMATES

Climate can be classified in several ways according to the specific factors that are taken into consideration. The surface of the earth receives its heat from the sun and so the earlier systems of classification were based largely upon the amount of daylight which different parts of the earth received throughout the year. One of the ways in which this was done was to divide the earth's surface into the following zones :—

(1) a *torrid* or *tropical* zone lying between the tropics of Cancer and Capricorn, *i.e.*, between lat. $23\frac{1}{2}°N$ and $23\frac{1}{2}°S$. This includes all places over which the sun is vertical at least once in the year;

(2) two *temperate* zones, lying between the tropic of Cancer and lat. $66\frac{1}{2}°N$, and between the tropic of Capricorn and lat. $66\frac{1}{2}°S$. In these zones the sun's rays are never vertical, but the sun rises and sets once in every 24 hours;

(3) the two *polar* or *frigid* zones, where the days and nights are sometimes more than 24 hours long.

In this classification countries having very dissimilar climates are included in the same zone since it does not take into consideration many of the circumstances modifying temperature or of the influence of prevailing winds.

Another classification is based on the great wind belts of the world, since climate is largely dependent on rainfall which in its turn is controlled by the relative humidity and direction of the prevailing winds. According to this scheme, the "tropical" zone includes the equatorial belt of calms, and the regions over which the trade winds blow; the "temperate" zones similarly fall in the latitudes affected by the westerlies. Here again, the boundaries of the wind belts are somewhat indefinite at all times, and shift according to the seasons.

Yet another classification proposed is based on temperature. According to this, the *hot belt* is bounded by the two mean annual isotherms of $20°C$; two *temperate* zones on either side of it, the polar limits of which are fixed by the isotherm $10°C$ for the warmest month; and two *polar* zones.

In each of the climatic zones so far defined, there exists a variety of climatic conditions due mainly to nearness or otherwise to the ocean, to the direction of prevailing winds, and to differences in elevation of the land. It is necessary, therefore, to distinguish in each zone an *oceanic* and a *continental* type of climate; with the intermediate variety known as the *littoral* (shore), and the extreme continental condition a *desert* climate.

Types of Climate

Equatorial Belt: The equatorial belt of calms is always hot and rainy. Dense tropical jungle is the characteristic vegetation.

Trade Wind Belts: The trade winds blow from cooler to warmer regions and so pick up much moisture when passing over the sea, which is condensed when the winds blow over rising lands. Hence coasts which face eastward in these zones have heavy rainfall. In blowing across continents, however, the trade winds become very dry winds, and so nearly all the great deserts of the world lie on the western margins of continents in the trade-wind zones.

Monsoon Region: In the region where monsoons are well developed there are generally three seasons in the year—a hot dry spring, a hot very rainy summer, and a cool winter with little rain. The combination of heavy rainfall with high temperature makes the monsoon countries perhaps the most productive in the world.

Horse Latitudes: The outer or temperate margins of the trade wind belts have generally a rather dry climate with considerable range of temperature. They are transitional between the desert and the temperate forest, and contain natural grass lands *i.e.*, the *steppes* of south-eastern Russia and south-western Asia, and the *prairies* of the middle United States.

Temperate Climates: In the north temperate zone the weather is largely determined by cyclonic disturbances. The rainfall is fairly evenly distributed throughout the year. This is a zone in which forests abound. The south temperate zone is somewhat cooler than the north.

Arctic Climates: At the time of the "midnight sun" *i.e.*, in summer, places near the Arctic circle have a cool damp climate, with frequent rain. The ground is generally swampy. In winter, when the sun has set, not to rise again till next spring, the ground is deeply frozen and covered with snow, while the sea is ice-bound. The frozen moss-covered marshes of the Arctic regions are known as *tundras*.

CLIMATE OF INDIA

India has a great diversity of climates and the meteorological conditions in different parts of the country present many contrasts. Punjab, for instance, has a continental climate with blazing heat in summer and freezing cold in winter, while Kerala has a tropical maritime climate with very little change in temperature and humidity throughout the year. Assam in the east is extremely damp whereas Rajasthan in the west is very arid. In the Thar desert the average annual rainfall is less than 13 cm, while at Cherrapunji in Assam the rainfall is as much as 1,080 cm.

The climate of India is largely dependent on conditions outside its geographical limits. The cold weather rain and snow-fall, for example, are related to the shallow low-pressure systems which arise northwest of India as far away as the eastern Mediterranean region. Similarly, the distribution of rainfall in the summer monsoon season depends upon the pressure and temperature conditions in southern Asia, the Indian Ocean, and the China Seas.

The most important feature of the climate of India is the alternation of seasons known as the monsoons. During the winter months the general air-flow over India is from land to sea as the northeast monsoon. The Asiatic cold air hardly ever seeps into India, the Himalayas acting as an effective barrier. The Bay of Bengal, Arabian Sea and the Indian Ocean are mostly affected by the air originating over the subtropical high pressure calms then located over the north of India. Since these winds originate over land they are mainly dry. In the summer months, the winds blow from sea to land as the southwest monsoon. Since these winds originate over the sea, they give rise to a season characterised by high humidity and frequent rain. During the winter months the land-mass of Central and South Asia is about 8°—14° C cooler than the Pacific and the Atlantic Ocean areas in the same latitudes, while in summer this land area is 5°— 8° C warmer than the sea. These differences are the main cause of the monsoons.

The physical features of India have a great influence on its climate. Heavy rainfall occurs on the windward side of the Western Ghats, the hills of Assam, and the Himalayas. The

iinfall is moderate in the plateau of the Peninsula and the Ganga
plains.   Southern Punjab and western Rajasthan are the driest
regions.

Between the two principal monsoon seasons there are two
transitional periods—the hot weather before the beginning of the
southwest monsoon, and the retreating southwest monsoon season.
Four principal seasons can, therefore, be recognised in India :—

1.   Cold weather season, December to February
2.   Hot weather season, March to May
3.   Southwest monsoon season, June to September
4.   Retreating southwest monsoon season, October to
     November.

1.   *The cold weather season:* This season commences in December,
and by January when temperatures in Asia are lowest, the
northeast monsoon prevails over the Indian land and sea areas.
Clear skies, fine weather, light northerly winds, low temperature
and humidity, are characteristic of the weather in India from
December to February.   Occasionally there are shallow cyclonic
depressions which travel from west to east across northern India
giving rise to heavy rains in the Punjab plains and considerable
snowfall in Kashmir.   Generally, during this season, rainfall is
greatest in the northwest of India and decreases towards the south
and east; the temperature is lower in the northwest than in the
east and south.

The average winter conditions over India in January which is a
typical cold weather month are depicted in Fig. 14.

2.   *The hot weather season:*   There is a continuous and rapid
rise of temperature and fall of barometric pressure in north India
from March to May, and a decrease of temperature in the southern
Indian Ocean during these months.   In March, the highest day
temperatures of about 38° C occur in the Deccan plateau, and in
April, Gujarat and Madhya Pradesh experience temperatures of
38° to 43° C.   In May, the highest temperatures occur in north
India, specially in the desert regions of the northwest, where the
maximum temperature may be over 48° C, and dust storms are of
common occurrence.   The area of lowest air pressure   stretches

from northwest India to Chota Nagpur which causes southern winds across the West Bengal coast, and northwesterly winds across the Bombay coast, which often result in violent winds, torrential rain, and hail. In West Bengal, these "Nor'-westers" as they are called, often attain the intensity of tornadoes and hence, are very destructive.

Fig. 15. illustrates the general meteorological conditions during April, the representative month of the season.

3. *The southwest monsoon season:* At the end of May, a fairly deep low pressure area extends from west Rajasthan to West Bengal. The southeast trade winds from the south of the equator blow northwards into the Bay of Bengal and the Arabian Sea; these are influenced by the air circulation over India and deflected inland as southwesterly winds which give rise to the cool and humid southwest monsoon.

The southwest monsoon bursts on the Kerala coast at the beginning of June. The monsoon gradually extends northwards and spreads over most of India by the end of June. June and July constitute an important season for India since agriculture depends mainly on the amount and distribution of rainfall during these two months.

A part of the monsoon wind advancing northwards from the Bay of Bengal towards Burma is deflected by the Arakan hills westwards up the Ganga plain; hence, the monsoon winds here are more from southeast and south than from southwest. After crossing the deltaic coast of Bengal, the monsoon winds are forced up the Assam and Chittagong hills and very heavy rainfall results in this region. Part of the monsoon current is turned wes wards by the Himalayan ranges and consequently all along their lower slopes from Sikkim to Kashmir there is almost continual rainfall during this monsoon season.

The southwest monsoon winds of the Arabian Sea are obstructed by the Western Ghats and hence there is heavy rainfall in the coastal region west of the Ghats. After crossing the Ghats, the monsoon advances over the Deccan plateau and Madhya Pradesh, and meets the current from the Bay of Bengal. Another part of

CHAPTER XXI

VEGETATION IN RELATION TO CLIMATE

TYPES OF VEGETATION

THE *vegetation* of a particular region may be regarded as the community of plants, which includes trees and grasses, that covers the area and gives it a distinct character. The types of vegetation depend on the appearance of the plant cover *e.g.*, forest and woodland, grassland, and desert. There is no sharp boundary between these types and they merge imperceptibly one into another. The gradual change from one distinct type to another is largely the result of the amount and distribution of rainfall during the year. Some differentiation of vegetation is dependent upon the temperature. Soil is also a factor to be considered.

The relation between climate and vegetation is of great significance. Given suitable growing temperatures, the most important factor in plant growth is the incidence of rainfall. In regions where there is not much rainfall, the incidence and length of a dry season is of great importance in determining the type of vegetation. With increasing length of the dry season, forest gives place to woodland and scrub, and they in turn to grassland and desert.

The general distribution of plant types has a direct relation to the climatic zones. The changes in climate which occur between the base and the summit of a mountain naturally influence the plant life, so that on ascending a high mountain in the tropics one meets with a succession of plant types somewhat similar to the order in which they would be met with, if one travelled towards the poles.

In forests and woodlands the predominant vegetation consists of woody plants like trees. *Forest* is an assemblage of trees in such close growth that their tops touch one another. In *woodland* there is considerable development of shrubs which isolate the taller trees. *Scrub* is vegetation where trees are few in number and occur in the Arabian Sea branch of the monsoon crosses the coast of Saurashtra and Kutch and reaches the Aravalli hills after passing over the arid zone of Rajasthan. On reaching eastern Punjab these winds join the current deflected westwards from the Bay of Bengal, and produce moderate to heavy rain in the western Himalayas, eastern Punjab, and east Rajasthan.

In general, the strength of the southwest monsoon and the associated rainfall increase from June to July and remain fairly steady in August. The monsoon retreats from northern India in the second week of September.

Fig. 16 giving the mean meteorological conditions in July illustrates the characteristics of the southwest monsoon season.

4. *The retreating southwest monsoon season :* Transitional conditions leading up to the dry winter season are prevalent in October and November. During this season there is dry weather in northern India, but there is general rainfall in the coastal districts of Madras State and over the eastern half of the Peninsula where it is known as the *northeast monsoon* rains. Cyclonic storms often form in the Bay of Bengal, and they generally advance towards the east coast of the Peninsula.

The general meteorological features of this season are depicted in Fig 17 which gives the average conditions prevalent in October.

scattered clumps along with lower woody plants and grasses. Trees may be differentiated into *deciduous*, with a seasonal leaf fall, and *evergreen*, which lose their leaves continuously but never all at one time. Another distinction depends upon the shape of the leaves of the tree, some having broad leaves and others needle leaves. Broad leaves are not solely characteristic of deciduous trees, as many broad-leaved trees are evergreen. On the other hand, most coniferous trees have needle leaves.

CHIEF ZONES OF VEGETATION

The Temperate Forests : Forests cover most of the belt which roughly corresponds with the isotherm of 10°C for the warmest month, and where there is fairly abundant rainfall. In the warmer temperate regions most of the trees have broad leaves which transpire freely when exposed to light; such trees in order to minimise the loss of water during winter, shed their leaves before winter and are known as deciduous. Typical examples are elm, fig, and oak. The cool temperate regions are characterised by xerophytic trees such as the conifers which have leaves specially adapted to restrict transpiration, and so their foliage is retained through the winter and at elevations where most of the broad-leaved trees are not able to survive. Examples of such conifers are pines, firs, cedars, cypresses, junipers, spruces etc. Their leaves are more or less needle-shaped and leathery. Coniferous forests are characteristic of the cool temperate regions and are found in latitudes which reach northwards to the tree limit that is determined by low temperatures. In coniferous forests there is little undergrowth as compared with the deciduous hardwood forests which have many shrubs between the trees. The conifers abound in the Himalayas.

The Tropical Forests : In the equatorial belt of climate, there is heavy rainfall with a continuously high temperature and hence, in the lowlands and in the valleys there is a luxuriant growth of vegetation forming dense forests. Because of the regular and adequate supply of water to the roots, all serious interruptions to growth are avoided and the plants are mainly *perennials*, that is, they live on from year to year. Among perennial plants, trees are the dominant type, so that well-watered countries in the tropical and temperate zones are naturally afforested. Parts of the Kerala State to some extent exhibit these characteristics. Among the economically important plants, mention may be made of the rubber tree and those yielding valuable timber such as ebony, mahogany, and rosewood. Winding and coiling creepers and climbers (known as lianas) are characteristic of these forests. The climatic conditions are suitable for the growth of palms, plantain trees, bamboos, orchids, cycads, and screw-pines. Among cultivated plants, the more delicate spices, nutmegs, cloves, and cinnamon, are restricted to this region.

Savannahs: Intermediate between the tropical forests and the dry deserts of the trade-wind belts are regions which receive only a moderate rainfall with a regularly recurring dry season. In such countries trees are scarcer, and their place is taken by herbaceous plants, chiefly *annuals*. The plants are active only during the moist season towards the end of which they produce seeds, or else tubers, bulbs, etc., capable of withstanding the coming drought. The plants then die but their seeds, bulbs, etc., survive and grow up when the necessary moisture is again available. *Grasses* are generally the most successful of herbaceous plants and they form the greater part of the vegetation of regions having this type of climate. Dry forest and scrub are often associated with grasses, and they occupy areas often referred to as savannahs. Savannah in the strict sense of the term means a treeless plain.

Grasslands: This type of vegetation is composed essentially of perennial grasses in tufts which form a fairly continuous cover to the land surface. Such are the *steppe* lands of Russia and the *prairies* of America. The most suitable areas for the development of natural grasslands are the continental interiors since they rarely have drought in summer.

The climate of parts of Peninsular India is very favourable for the growth of grasses. In the Satpura districts, as well as in the Nilgiri hills where the rainfall is abundant and the winters are mild, and also in the western Deccan and on the Shillong plateau, there are rich *meadow grasses*.

The plants known as *cereals* are grasses with edible seeds, and it is the grasslands which are the principal sources of this most important food product.   Rice, however, requires a higher temperature and a more moist climate than wheat, and is grown chiefly in the deltaic lowlands of India such as those of the rivers Ganga, Godavari, Krishna, and Cauvery.   Millet is grown chiefly in the drier regions of the Deccan.   Other conditions being favourable, the principal wheat belt lies between lat. 40° and 52°, though it is cultivated both to the north and to the south of this belt.   Barley grows over a much wider belt both pole-ward and equator-ward; oats grow north of wheat, and corn (maize) grows south of it.

As the forest regions of the temperate or cooler regions are succeeded to the leeward by the grasslands, so these in their turn give place on their "continental" side to deserts, especially where surrounding high land has co-operated with distance from the sea in drying the prevailing winds.

Desert Vegetation: Under desert conditions, aridity restricts vegetation so much that a complete plant cover is absent.   Whilst in some desert areas plant growth is almost impossible because of extreme aridity, most deserts have a representative flora.   The areas of waterless deserts are very limited, and many areas noted as deserts on maps are really semi-desert from the point of view of vegetation.   A characteristic feature of this vegetation is that each plant is separated from its neighbours by great distances.

More than half the land lying in the trade-wind belts consists of deserts.   The scanty vegetation is predominantly *xerophytic* in character i.e., they are adapted for living under drought conditions, so that in order to minimise loss of water by transpiration, the modified leaves are succulent, fleshy, leathery, hairy, covered with wax, needle-shaped, very small, or even absent altogether. Along the margins of the deserts where there is a little more rainfall, thorny plants like acacias are common.   The date palm grows in the oases and on the margins of the rivers.

The arid region of Punjab and Rajasthan is known as the Thar desert, but detailed investigations of surface features, ground-water conditions, and vegetation, indicate that it is not really a desert in the true sense of the term. The eastern part is more humid, less sandy, and clothed with steppe vegetation.

VEGETATION IN INDIA

While dealing earlier in this chapter with the different climatic regions, reference has occasionally been made to the vegetation in India characteristic of such climatic conditions. A brief description will now be given of some of the more important floristic regions of India.

The location of India between 8°4′N and 37°6′ N gives this country considerable latitudinal spread, and consequently, a wide range of temperature conditions. There is also great variation in altitudes, the range being from sea-level to the loftiest mountains of the world. Therefore, between the coastal plains and the mountains of India, we have practically all the climatic zones from the torrid to the arctic. While plant activity is continuous in the plains, the highest peaks of the Himalayas are above the limits of vegetation and covered with perpetual snow. The humidity and rainfall range from the lowest in the desert of Rajasthan to the highest in the hills of Assam where Cherrapunji with an annual rainfall of nearly 1,080 cm has the reputation of being the wettest spot in the world.

From the point of their relatively low rainfall and humidity, the Deccan, the Indus plain, and the Western Himalayas show a marked contrast with Malabar, Lower Ganga plain, Assam, and the Eastern Himalayas. Altitude is the chief factor in the characterisation of the vegetation on the Himalayas.

Malabar Region: This comprises the excessively humid (rainfall more than 200 cm) belt of mountain country running parallel to the west coast of the Peninsula. Except in the north, the Western Ghats often rise abruptly from the flat coast. Its steep western face is clothed with a luxuriant evergreen forest. There are many varieties of palms. Of the commercial crops the most important are betel-nut, cocoanut, palmyra, pepper, coffee, and tea. Rubber, cashew nut, and eucalyptus have been introduced successfully in suitable areas of this region; rubber in the very humid areas, cashew nut along the coast, and eucalyptus in the Nilgiri and other hills,

The cocoanut forms a major element in the economy of Malabar, and this palm lines the lagoons and canals of the coast.

Assam Region: Over the greater part of this region the rainfall exceeds 200 cm. The vegetation is luxuriant and the valleys, where they are not under tea or agricultural crops, are clothed with expanses of savannah grasses or with dense forests of an evergreen type.

The hill forests of the Assam region approximate in type to those of the Eastern Himalayan region, except that there is no alpine zone. These hill forests may be classified broadly into evergreen forests, broad-leaved forests, and pine forests. The hill tops of Assam, like those of the Nilgiris, are open grasslands with trees and shrubs identical with or closely related to those of the Nilgiris.

Eastern Himalayan Region: This region extending from Sikkim eastwards, is the most humid portion of the Himalayan range. Darjeeling, Kurseong, and other places are located in this area. The Eastern Himalayan ranges being at a somewhat lower altitude than parts of the Western Himalayas, are relatively warmer, and the timber line, alpine flora, and snowline are at somewhat higher altitudes than in the Western Himalayas.

The temperate zone of the Eastern Himalayas extends from 1,500 to 3,650 m. In the lower belt of this zone below 2,750 m occur a large number of different broad-leaved species, oaks, laurels, maples, alder, birch, etc. Conifers occur mostly above 2,750 m. Among other plants in this zone may be mentioned rhododendrons and dwarf willows. The bamboo forms a dense growth in places. Two palms also occur in this zone—one is a scandent rattan, and the other a fan palm.

The alpine zone extends from 3,650 m to about 4,900 m. Several species of rhododendrons occur here, and junipers of the upper temperate zone also extend high into this zone.

Western Himalayan Region: This comprises the sub-Himalayan tract, and the Himalayan range from Kumaun to Kashmir. In general, the Western Himalayas are much cooler and drier than the Eastern. The rainfall varies from 100 to 200 cm. The inner valleys and the north-western areas of this region have a dry climate. Naini Tal, Mussoorie, Simla, and Kashmir are in this region.

The sub-montane zone and lower hills up to 1,500 m contain an almost continuous belt of sal forest in the eastern part of the region. Savannah lands break up the sal belt at intervals. In the western part of the region, the forest becomes drier in character, and xerophytic plants occur. Among palms, only five species occur in contrast with several in the Eastern Himalayas.

The temperate zone extending from 1,500 m to 3,650 m, contains extensive forests of conifers and broad-leaved temperate trees. Pine prevails in the lower elevations. Soon it gives place to deodar and blue pine; higher up, spruce and silver fir form forests of large extent between 2,400 m and 3,350 m. Of other conifers, the yew is common in some localities. Cypress is found locally, and the edible pine occurs in the dry valleys. Oaks, maples, horse chestnut, poplar, elm, alder, and birch occur.

The alpine zone extends from the upper limit of the temperate zone to about 4,600 m. The characteristic trees of this zone are the high-level silver fir, the silver birch, and junipers.

CHAPTER XXII

SOIL EROSION AND ITS EFFECTS

SOIL EROSION

SOIL EROSION is a natural process which has gone on during the geological ages, but there is a balance in nature which has resulted in the formation of soil from the parent rock. The rich alluvial deltas of the world afford good examples. This balance has, however, been upset by man as a result of indiscriminate clearing of forests, senseless overgrazing of pasture lands, and haphazard drainage operations. Once this balance is destroyed, the rate of erosion is increased, and examples can be quoted from past history to show how such accelerated soil erosion was one of the chief contributory causes for the decay of some civilisations. Improper land use causes accelerated soil erosion and leads to the formation of gullies and ultimately, ravines. Soil erosion has been described as "creeping death," because, by depleting the land of its rich soil, it causes misery, poverty, and ultimate starvation to people.

Soil erosion has had devastating effects in West Bengal, Uttar Pradesh, Madhya Pradesh, Delhi, Rajasthan, and many other parts of India. In Punjab, excessive grazing by cattle destroyed the grass on the slopes of the hills. This destruction of the natural cover resulted in the rapid erosion of the soil. The Nilgiri Hills in Madras State have suffered greatly by soil erosion; the opening up of land for cultivation of potatoes, and clearance of forests to form plantations has resulted in considerable depletion of the soil. The problem is no less serious in Mysore State where forests have been denuded for timber and fuel, and overgrazing is widespread.

Ravines are widespread in some parts of North India. The aerial survey carried out in connection with the Chambal Development Scheme showed that the area containing ravines 4.5 to 6 m deep is nearly 1,25,000 acres in extent. In Madhya

Pradesh the area affected by ravines is mostly along the rivers Chambal, Kali Sind, and their tributaries. It is estimated that about 15 lakh acres of land must be affected by deep gullies and ravines. Out of this, about 6 lakh acres are in the three districts of Gwalior, Morena and Bhind. In Uttar Pradesh, the Indo-Gangetic alluvium has been deeply dissected by the Jamuna, Chambal, Gomati, and their tributaries.

In Madras, ravine formation is common in the South Arcot, North Arcot, Kanyakumari, Tiruchi, Chingleput, Salem, and Coimbatore districts.

In West Bengal, there are numerous gullies and ravines in the upper catchment areas of Kangsabati river in the Purulia district.

There are no accurate statistics of the total area affected by soil erosion in India but it has been estimated that at least 1,00,000 acres are permanently lost to cultivation and a much larger area is rendered less productive every year by erosion. Soil erosion is, therefore, a national menace and systematic and scientific attempts must be made to combat and prevent the spread of this insidious evil.

As the result of the combined influence of weathering agents, a soil profile is developed consisting of three distinct layers which from below upwards are : (1) the solid rock, (2) the sub-soil formed by blocks and boulders of rocks, and (3) the top soil consisting of few small fragments of rocks in a matrix of sand or sandy clay, and in which are stored the organic matter, chemicals and nutriments which sustain plant growth. The average thickness of soil varies between 20 and 30 cm, and it is this layer that is responsible for all plant growth.

EFFECTS OF EROSION

In nature, there is an equilibrium between the climate (chiefly rainfall and temperature) of a place, and the cover of vegetation that protects the layer of soil. Grass, shrubs, and trees retard the transportation of soil. Some amount of erosion does take place even under this natural cover, but it is very slow and is compensated by the formation of fresh soil by the ordinary processes of natural weathering. This type of erosion is, therefore, not of much consequence, because there is a balance between the disintegration of rocks and the subsequent formation of soil. It is when the rate of change is upset that this balance is destroyed and accelerated erosion takes place. Man is mainly responsible for setting in motion these changes. Deforestation, cultivation on steep slopes, unrestricted grazing, indiscriminate drainage operations, denuding fires—these are some of the causes for the ultimate devastation of good lands by soil erosion.

When rain falls on land covered with thick vegetation, the clear water sinks slowly into the soil; but when it falls on bare soil, the impact causes the fine soil particles to go into suspension, and this results in a muddy flow of water along the surface. As the volume of water increases, the velocity also increases and the erosive power becomes greater. A heavy downpour of rain is, therefore, capable of tearing up the surface soil from unprotected slopes and carrying it away in muddy streams.

This type of soil denudation results in severe floods and increased scouring. Such floods are a source of danger for road and rail bridges, irrigation and navigation channels, storage reservoirs, hydro-electric projects, and water-supply and pumping stations. It has been proved by observation in the United States of America that during recent years, floods in many parts of the country have increased in frequency, volume, and velocity. This has been attributed to the accelerated run-off caused by the removal of the vegetation cover by overgrazing and disafforestation.

The material carried by storm water clogs streams and rivers, and the carrying capacity of drainage streams is reduced, and the efficiency of irrigation systems is lowered. Heavy deposits of sand and silt in river beds in alluvial tracts cause a rise in flood levels, and result in serious damage to agricultural lands. The bed of the Cauvery in the Tiruchirapalli and Thanjavur districts of Madras State, has gradually risen, and many of the old irrigation sluices and drainage inlets are getting blocked by accumulation of sand in the river bed.

Silting of tanks is another serious consequence of soil erosion.

There is a natural downward flow of soil due to gravity, and any reservoir, pond, or lake will gradually get filled up. In this way, many of the tanks in South India are getting rapidly silted. If, after rains, a tank is filled with highly coloured water, that is a sure sign that soil erosion is doing its destructive work. This calls for remedial action in order to prevent the storage capacity of reservoirs and tanks being greatly diminished.

Part of the rain-water which falls on the surface of the earth percolates into the earth by being absorbed by the soil. This water follows a downward course and helps to raise the level of the water-table. Percolation is greatly aided by a cover of vegetation. Dead leaves of trees and the grass of pasture lands check the flow of water and help in its being absorbed by the soil. This is caused by the water being held in contact with the soil for a longer period so that it can gradually soak in. Absorption is thus increased and the run-off reduced, and this has a very beneficial effect on crop yield. Also, by raising the water-table more water is made available for irrigation purposes.

Erosion produces three types of losses—(1) valuable plant food is carried away in solution, (2) fine silt and (3) in many cases the soil itself is removed by scouring.

TYPES OF EROSION

The two most active agents of erosion are wind and water. Wind erosion is prominent in arid and semi-arid regions. Light soils which are loamy and sandy are more susceptible to wind erosion than heavier soils.

Wind erosion is active in arid lands having very little rainfall (125 mm to 250 mm annually), and in areas adjoining rivers, lakes, or sea. Wind carries away sand in what are known as drifts. Sand drifts from deserts spread over adjoining cultivated lands and destroy their fertility.

The arid region in north-west India which covers an area of about 1,05,000 km² extending over parts of Gujarat, Punjab and Rajasthan States, is subject to intense wind erosion. This whole area is a sandy plain though the soil improves in fertility from west to east. On the rocky hills and plateaus, the soil layer is thin and devoid of vegetation, hence the top soil is blown away or washed down.

Erosion due to water is more serious and occurs extensively in all parts of India. Water erosion manifests itself in four forms: (1) surface or sheet erosion, (2) finger gullying, (3) gully erosion, and (4) stream erosion.

Sheet Erosion: The movement of run-off water and eroded soil takes place in sheets, the amount of soil being removed from equal areas being approximately the same. This is a very insidious process because the damage is not easily noticeable. With every heavy shower the cream of the top soil is uniformly skimmed off. After some time, due to complete exhaustion, the colour of the soil becomes light and resembles the sub-soil. The production capacity of the land gets reduced due to loss of fertility of the soil.

Finger Gullying: Where fields are not quite smooth laterally, water concentrates into small rills and rivulets, which converge into bigger channels, and the channels in turn converge into hill-side ditches, the whole pattern resembling that of twigs, branches, and trunk of a tree. This represents an intermediate stage between sheet erosion and gully formation.

Gully Erosion: When finger gullying has advanced so much that the water channels are no longer interchangeable or easily obliterated, it develops into gully erosion. Gullies deepen and widen with every rainfall, and they can rapidly ravage the countryside. They cut up agricultural lands into small fragments and make them finally unfit for cultivation. The size and shape of gullies depend upon the soil, the sub-soil, slope of ground, rainfall, and the size and shape of the watershed. If hard rock is met with near the surface, the gullies are shallow and wide. If the sub-soil consists of plastic clay, shallow V-shaped gullies are formed. If the sub-soil is soft, then broad U-shaped gullies of great depth result. Gullies advance by lengthening, by enlargement, or by development of numerous side branches. Ordinarily when a gully cuts into the soil with an immediate drop of 3 or 4 m and gradually flattens out, a ravine is formed (*Plate 26*).   The depth of a ravine may be 30 m or more.

Stream Erosion: Erosion in valley streams, drainage courses, and in rivers in alluvial plains, takes the form of bank cutting, but bottom scour also occurs when gradients are steep, or when the volume of flow is increased.   Bank cutting is particularly noticeable on the outside bank at the beginning of bends in meandering streams.

RATE OF EROSION

The rate of erosion in a particular place is determined by the eroding power of water and wind, and the resisting power of the soil.   Where these are balanced we find virgin soil.   If, for any reason, the resisting power is lessened, the eroding power is automatically increased, and accelerated erosion is caused.

The physical and chemical characteristics of the soil greatly influence the amount and speed of run-off.   Factors having an important influence on the amount and rate of run-off are, intensity of rainfall on the catchment, size and shape of the catchment, slope of the land, vegetation on the catchment area, atmospheric conditions such as temperature, humidity, etc., and other miscellaneous factors.   Of these, rainfall and land slope are the only ones that cannot be modified much by acts of man.

The amount and rate of run-off naturally depend upon the amount, intensity, and duration of rainfall.   A heavy downpour within a short time causes as much damage as all the other rains during the year put together.   A gentle shower is absorbed easily by the soil and causes less damage than a heavy downpour.

Slope affects run-off by imparting velocity.   The steeper the slope, other things being equal, the less time there is for absorption and the faster is the run-off.   In the hilly tracts of the Nilgiris, cultivation of potatoes is done on very steep slopes without proper anti-erosive measures.   After the harvest of potatoes in July-August, the soil is loose and without a cover, and so the fields are subject to very severe erosion during the rainy period.

In a flat topography, numerous precipitous gullies are formed which cut their way through good agricultural land. Gullies are characterised by the undercutting erosive action of the waterfall at their heads.

Heavy soils like the black cotton soils are rich in clay and silt. They are highly retentive of moisture but are slow to absorb rain water. They are sticky when wet and hard when dry. By not being able to absorb the rain water as fast as it is received, there is excessive run-off which carries away the surface soil, and this results in excessive erosion of the black cotton soil.

Plant life plays a very important role in soil and water conservation. Leaves of shrubs and trees directly intercept, disperse, and evaporate falling rain drops. Close-growing grasses act as a protective cover against the violent impact of rainfall. The root systems have a binding effect on the surface layer of the soil.

Ruts and furrows caused by ploughing along the slope instead of across the slope accelerates erosion. Diversion of natural drainage courses by road or railway embankments and culverts may result in gullies. Storm-water drains along roads, and earth-cuttings from where material has been taken for road repairs, are frequently accompanied by erosion.

METHODS OF EROSION CONTROL

Soil erosion is the result of misuse of land and is, therefore, essentially a man-made problem. The natural limitations to which land could be put to use serve as the basis for all measures of soil conservation. The first step in any rational solution is to restrict open cultivated land to slopes and conditions where erosion can be held in check. This means that certain slopes are best suited for cultivated crops, steeper slopes are best suited for permanent pastures, and still steeper slopes are best suited for forests. The division between these cannot, of course, be a thin line but a border zone of considerable width and flexibility. Increased slope means increased velocity of run-off which results in rapid erosion. Because of this danger, lands should not be cultivated which are above a critical slope varying between 1 in 4 and 1 in 7 according to local conditions of soil and climate. Lands on steep gradients can be cultivated only after costly terracing; cultivation without terracing will rapidly end in depletion of the soil.

In many parts of India, there are two factors which have seriously affected the natural cover of land and given rise to extensive erosion. These are overgrazing and forest fires. Many of the hills bear a dry thorny scrub jungle with a medium grass cover which is the grazing ground of the neighbouring villages. The grass dries up during summer and the villagers set fire to it under the erroneous belief that when the monsoon breaks a luxuriant growth of new grass will shoot up. These fires spread very rapidly and burn everything on whole hillsides. The trees are subjected to severe burns, and the ground cover is destroyed. Rain falling on the exposed soil results in heavy run-off and sheet erosion. The lower reaches of the hill, where there has been intense over-grazing, are also subject to erosion. In this way forests and forest pastures gradually deteriorate through the years. Steps should be taken, therefore, to educate the villagers so that they will realise the serious consequences of overgrazing and forest fires.

All measures for erosion control depend mainly on three things :— (1) increasing absorption, (2) reducing the percentage of run-off, and (3) affording protection against damage by the residual run-off. Absorption may be increased by improving the infiltration rate of the soil, and by impounding the water where it falls, thus increasing the time of contact or the absorption opportunity. Contour bunding, contour trenching, terracing, regulated forestry, controlled grazing, revegetation, selective weeding, cover cropping, mixed farming, crop rotation, strip cropping etc., are some of the remedial measures which have to be adopted in order to reduce soil erosion and to increase crop production.

Gullying generally follows the loss of surface soil through sheet erosion. It is always better, if possible, to prevent the formation of gullies than to try to control them after they are formed. If a land is in varying stages of erosion, it is logical to protect first the best land from further loss, but it is more practical to begin with the gullies if they are not too far advanced.

Finger gullies can often be eliminated by diverting the water by terracing and cultivation. In bigger gullies, the erosive velocities are reduced by constructing a series of check dams which transform the longitudinal gradient of the gully from a uniform steep slope to a succession of "steps." These are of a temporary character and serve to retard erosion while vegetation for permanent control is becoming established. By building as many additonal check dams as may be necessary, the gully can be filled completely. Drainage should then be diverted by terraces, or the fill left under a cover of undisturbed turf to prevent a recurrence of scour.

Special attention should be paid to the upper end of the gully where an abrupt drop or overhanging bank is generally present. When water falls over this head bank, it strikes the bottom and scours in all directions. This soon causes the bank to be undermined more and more until a section caves off, and the process starts all over again. By this process, gullies have been known to advance into good land a distance of 20 m in one season, frequently where land slopes are flat enough to be otherwise stable. This type of waterfall erosion can be prevented by cutting back the head bank to a slope of about 30° and installing a flume of planks or galvanised irons; or by having the sides smoothened and the channel lined with rubble masonry or concrete. The most satisfactory way is to divert the run-off permanently to other outlets, so that the head banks of gullies on which terraces are built lose their power to cause further damage.

CHAPTER XXIII

STRUCTURE AND TOPOGRAPHY OF INDIA

THE TOPOGRAPHY of a country is carved out of materials of the earth's crust by the work of nature's sculptoring agents. While it is possible generally to appreciate landscape, the enjoyment of scenery is greatly enhanced by a knowledge of the way in which it originated and developed; for, every topographic feature which is present today on the face of the earth is the culmination of a long succession of geological events. The present is only a parenthesis in geological time, a link between the immense past and the unknown future.

ORIGIN OF THE INDIAN CONTINENT

India was part of Gondwanaland, the great Southern Continent, which broke up after the close of Palaeozoic time into huge continental blocks. These crustal slabs gradually drifted apart to form the present-day continents of Africa, Australia, Antarctica, and South America.

The Talchir Boulder Bed of glacial origin indicates that during the Permo-Carboniferous period India must have been situated far away from the equator. When Gondwanaland was fragmented, the Indian continent drifted northwards. This movement caused the Peninsular Indian block to plough into the Mediterranean Sea of Tethys causing the pile of geosynclinal sediments there to buckle up. There is evidence to show that the northern borders of the Peninsular block have been overridden by the much younger ranges of the Himalaya. The doubling of the sialic crust is responsible for the formation of the world's most elevated tableland in Tibet, the so-called "Roof of the World". The Himalayan ranges continued to be uplifted by a series of very severe convulsions.

These major crust movements were responsible for the sharply demarcated threefold structural and physiographical divisions of

India, each with its own characteristic features—the Peninsula, consisting mainly of Precambrian rocks in a stable shield area; the Extra-Peninsula, formed of a system of folded and faulted sedimentary beds which were deposited in a mediterranean sea; and an intermediate tectonic rift valley known as the Indo-Gangetic trough which is now filled with a thick deposit of alluvium. Fig. 18 depicts the main physiographic sub-divisions of India.

EXTRA-PENINSULAR REGION

The Himalaya is the world's highest mountain system. It is also the world's youngest and largest east-west mountain system. The Himalaya is structurally related to the foreland of India. It is a typical tectonic mountain which started to rise from the bottom of the Sea of Tethys about 50 to 60 million years ago. The uplift was gradual and lasted several million years and this accounts for the antecedent courses of many Himalayan rivers which, though they have their origin on the northern side of the ranges, flow south into India in steep-sided deep gorges right across the east-west trends of the high mountain ranges. The erosion of the river beds has kept pace with the slow uplift of the Himalayas.

There are two sharp bends of the Himalayan chain of mountains, one on the west near Nanga Parbat where the Indus takes a turn, and the other on the east near the Mishmi hills in Assam where the Brahmaputra takes a turn. These syntaxial bends are caused by the underthrust of the Peninsular block into the sedimentary formations constituting the Himalayas. The trends of the Himalayan ranges are convex towards the Peninsula and concave towards Tibet. Throughout the 2,400 km from Kashmir to Assam the curving trends of the Himalayas are controlled by the shape of the Gondwanaland block.

There are at least three major thrusts in the Siwalik and Lesser Himalayan zones. The southernmost of these is the Main Boundary Fault which separates the Siwaliks from the Tertiary and older rocks. To the north of the Tertiary belt in Kashmir is a zone containing sediments of Carboniferous to Eocene Age which have been folded and thrust over the foreland. Beyond this is the zone of nappes in which there are two or more important thrusts. Further north is the Central Himalayan range consisting of sediments intruded by large masses of granite which constitute some of the highest regions from the snow-capped peak of Everest to Nanga Parbat on the Indus. Though the granites are probably of different ages, many of them are considered to be Cainozoic. The crystalline core of the Central Himalayas represents the frontal part of Gondwanaland (Peninsular India) that was folded and caught in the nappe zone during the Himalayan orogenesis.

The vast recumbent structures of the Cainozoic Himalaya along with the Siwalik formations were thrown into convulsion again in the Plio-Pleistocene period, and certain of the movements continue to this day, as evidenced by the earthquakes in this region. North of the Main Boundary Fault, upheaval far exceeded even the mid-Cainozoic orogeny in violence. The old nappe structures were rejuvenated and new ones produced which reached forward far into the foreland.

There is also evidence of very late vertical movements. The Karewa series of Pleistocene lake and river deposits in the Kashmir valley have been tilted and elevated to between 1,500 and 1,800 m.

THE INDO-GANGETIC FORELAND

Between the Himalayan region and the Peninsula lies the Indo-Gangetic plain—a broad and monotonously level expanse, built up of recent alluvium through which the rivers flow sluggishly towards the seas. The plain is composed of layers of sand, clay, and occasional organic debris forming peat beds, of geologically very recent date (Pleistocene and Recent), filling up a deep depression. This depression, which can be described as a "fore-deep", is due to a sag in the northern flank of the Peninsula which developed contemporaneously with the uplift of the Himalayas.

The central and eastern parts of the plains have been built up by the Ganga and its tributaries which flow south-east. The western part in Punjab is the region where the tributaries of the Indus flow in a south-westerly direction. Though part of the

Indo-Gangetic plains, southern Punjab and specially west Rajasthan are subject to arid conditions and hence this region is passing today through a different landscape cycle.

PENINSULAR INDIA

Shield Area: The Peninsula is structurally, stratigraphically, and physiographically, quite a contrast to the above two divisions of India. It represents a stable block of the earth's crust which has remained unaffected by orogenic or mountain-building movements since practically the close of the Precambrian era. The later changes which have taken place are mainly epeirogenic or plateau-building movements by which some parts have risen or sunk in relation to others. The Peninsula is a shield area composed of some of the oldest rocks of the earth's crust which have undergone much crushing and metamorphism. On this basement of crystalline rocks lie some later sediments and extensive lava flows (Deccan Traps).

The Peninsula has been exposed from ancient times to the agents of erosion and is at present an extensive plateau approaching peneplanation. The roots of old mountains are discernible, but the present-day elevations are erosion remnants left in various stages of denudation.

The Western Ghats which run almost parallel to the west coast from the Tapti valley to Cape Comorin, are the most important hill ranges of the Peninsula. They are composed in the north of Deccan Traps and in the south of Precambrian gneisses and schists. The topography of the Trap region is distinctive—the hills are flat-topped and the sides are formed of a series of step-like terraces. Though situated close to the Arabian Sea, the Western Ghats form the real watershed of the Peninsula, and most of the rivers flow eastwards into the Bay of Bengal.

The Eastern Ghats are formed of detached hill-ranges composed of high grade metamorphic rocks. Evidences of uplift are seen in the hills north of the Krishna river. The Nilgiri is the hilly region where the Eastern and Western Ghats meet.

The Vindhya mountains are a series of plateaus formed of

bedded quartzites. Together with the Satpuras, they form the watershed of central India.

The Aravalli mountains are the remnants of ancient ranges of tectonic origin. They form the major watershed of northern India, separating the drainage of the Ganga river system from that of the Indus, the former flowing into the Bay of Bengal, and the latter into the Arabian Sea.

Geological Structure: The discovery of radioactivity has had a remarkable effect on certain aspects of geological investigation. One of the problems which was not soluble by ordinary geological methods was the determination of the precise ages of unfossiliferous rocks. Radioactivity is the process whereby the nuclei of certain elements spontaneously emit particles, and in so doing produce new elements. Now, the rate at which a radioactive element "decays" and produces a new element is constant and unaffected by any known chemical or physical agency. Natural minerals in rocks, therefore, which contain radioactive elements are unceasingly producing and storing away these end-products. At any instant during this process of conversion, therefore, there will be a definite ratio between the original element and the decay product. This ratio depends on the length of time the radioactive decay has been going on, and so serves as an index to the age of the mineral. Most of the minerals which are suitable for such age determinations are found in pegmatites which are commonly associated with granites that were formed within orogenic belts towards the close of the major orogenies. The granites as well as the associated pegmatites can be dated by determining the age of certain minerals in them like micas and potash feldspars. The age of the granite will give the date of the closing phases of the orogeny in which it is found. Regional strikes of rock formations can then be related to the orogenies, and in this way correlations can be made and the order of succession of rock formations determined.

Considering the size of Peninsular India and the complexity of the composition and structure of the different Precambrian rocks in it, there are not many age determinations, but even the few that we have, have thrown considerable light on the relative ages of the structural units of this vast period of geological time. Fig. 19 is a simplified structural map of Peninsular India showing the main trends of the important orogenic belts and their ages. It will be seen that the chief regional strikes are represented by the Dharwar Schist belts (N.N.W.-S.S.E.), the Eastern Ghats belt (N.E.-S.W.), the Satpura belt (W.S.W.-E.N.E.), and the Aravalli and Delhi belts (N.E.-S.W.).

The radiometric ages supported by structural evidence indicate that Peninsular India like other shield areas of the world displays an ingrained pattern of successive orogenic belts. The following orogenic cycles can be recognised :

Dharwar cycle	—	—	2,600	million years
Iron-ore cycle	—	—	2,000	,,
Eastern Ghats cycle	—	—	1,600	,,
Satpura cycle	—	—	1,000	,,
Delhi cycle	—	—	700	,,

Erosion Surfaces: Gondwanaland, of which India was a part, had been exposed to erosion for quite a long period of geological time, and the surface of the land reduced to a peneplain. About 175 million years ago this Southern Continent started breaking up, and large crustal blocks gradually drifted away. Though isolated, the Gondwana erosion surface can be identified both in Africa and India. Remnants of this surface at an elevation of about 2,600 m are preserved in the high plateaus on the Nilgiri, Cardamom, and Kodaikanal hills in south India.

Erosion is a continuous process and several later surfaces can be noticed. A post-Gondwana erosional surface can be inferred from the imperfect bevelling seen near Ootacamund on the Nilgiri hills at an elevation of about 2,000 m which corresponds to some of the higher levels on the residual hills of the Eastern Ghats.

The west coast of the Peninsula represents the rift along which India broke off from Africa. This scarp which must once have been lapped by the sea, was acted upon by erosional agents, and continued to retreat landward. The Western Ghats scarp was believed to be a fault scarp but is now considered to be a normal erosional feature connected with pediplanation.

Coeval with the upheaval of the Himalayas during the mid-Cainozoic period there was a major regional upwarp of the Peninsula whereby the peneplaned surface was raised to a height of about 900 m. This surface has been lowered in two stages, for we now have an erosion surface at an elevation of about 600 m which is seen in northern Mysore State, and a still lower surface at about 400 m which is confined to the broad alluvial valleys of the Krishna and its tributaries.

Some local upwarps have affected the dissected plateau surfaces during the Late Cainozoic. Their main effects are seen on the drainage such as rejuvenation, accelerated valley erosion and related river capture.

GLOSSARY

Ablation — The process by which glacier ice below the snow line is wasted by evaporation and melting.

Abrasion — Erosion of rock material by friction of solid particles carried by water, ice, wind, or gravity.

Aftershock — An earthquake that follows a larger earthquake and originates at or near the focus of the larger earthquake. Major shallow earthquakes are often followed by many aftershocks which may continue for many days or even months.

Alluvial fan — The land counterpart of a delta. An assemblage of sediments marking the place where a stream moves from a steep gradient to a flatter gradient and suddenly loses its transporting power. Typical of arid and semi-arid climates, but not confined to them.

Alpine glacier — A glacier confined to a stream valley. Usually fed from a cirque. Also called *valley glacier* or *mountain glacier*.

Antecedent stream — A stream that maintains after uplift the same course it originally followed prior to uplift.

Anticline — A fold whose limbs dip outward away from one another. It is the reverse of a *syncline*.

Aquifer — A permeable material through which ground-water moves.

Arête — A narrow, saw-toothed ridge formed by cirques developing from opposite sides into the ridge.

Arroyo — Flat-floored, vertically walled channel of an intermittent stream typical of semi-arid climates.

Artesian water — Water that is under pressure when tapped by a well and is able to rise above the level at which it is first met with.

Atoll — A ring of low coral islands arranged around a central lagoon.

Barchan—A crescent-shaped dune with wings or horns pointing downwind which has a gentle windward slope and steep lee slope inside the horns.

Barrier reef—A reef that is separated from a landmass by a lagoon of varying width and depth opening to the sea through gaps in the reef.

Basalt—Fine-grained dark coloured igneous rock.

Basaltic layer—An inner layer of the earth's crust composed of basalt which underlies the oceans and granitic continents.

Base level—For a stream, a level below which it cannot erode. Ultimate base level for a stream is sea level.

For a *region*, a plane extending inland from sea level sloping gently upward from the sea. Erosion of the land progresses toward this plane, but seldom, if ever, quite reaches it.

Batholith—A discordant igneous intrusion that increases in size downward, has no determinable floor, and shows an area of surface exposure exceeding 100 square kilometres.

Bay barrier—A sandy beach built up across the mouth of a bay, so that the bay is no longer connected to the main body of water.

Bed load—Material in movement along a stream bed, or, if wind is the moving agency, along the surface. Contrast with material carried in suspension or solution.

Beheaded stream—The lower section of a stream that has lost its upper portion through stream capture or piracy.

Bergschrund—The gap or crevasse between glacier ice and the headwall of a cirque.

Body wave—Push-pull or shake earthquake wave that travels through the body of a medium, as distinguished from waves that travel along a free surface.

Braided stream—A complex tangle of converging and diverging stream channels separated by sand bars or islands. Characteristic of flood plains where the amount of debris is large in relation to the discharge.

Caldera — A roughly circular, steep-sided basin generally at the summit of a volcano with a diameter at least three or four times its depth.

Calving — As applied to glacier ice, the process by which a glacier that terminates in a body of water breaks away in large blocks. Such blocks form the icebergs of polar seas.

Capacity — The amount of material that a transporting agency such as a stream, a glacier, or the wind can carry under a particular set of conditions.

Central vent — An opening in the earth's crust, roughly circular, from which magmatic products are extruded. A volcano is an accumulation of material around a central vent.

Chemical weathering — The weathering of rock material by chemical processes that transform the original material into new chemical combinations.

Cinder cone — Built exclusively or in large part of pyroclastic ejecta dominated by cinders. Parasitic to a major volcano, it seldom exceeds 450 m in height.

Cirque — A steep-walled depression in a mountainside at high elevation, formed by ice-plucking and frost action, and shaped like a half-amphitheatre. Serves as principal gathering ground for the ice of a valley glacier.

Col — A pass through a mountain ridge. Created by the enlargement of two cirques on opposite sides of the ridge until their headwalls meet and are broken down.

Compaction — Reduction in pore space between individual grains as a result of pressure of overlying sediments or pressures resulting from earth movement.

Competence — The maximum size of particle that a transporting agency such as a stream, a glacier, or the wind, can move.

Composite volcanic cone — Composed of interbedded volcanic flows and pyroclastic material.

Cone sheet — A dyke that is part of a concentric set that dips inward, like an inverted cone.

Connate water — Water that was trapped in a sedimentary deposit at the time the deposit was laid down.

Consequent stream—A stream that is following a course that is a direct consequence of the original slope of the surface on which it developed.

Continental crust—Portion of the earth's crust composed of an upper layer of sialic rock, 15 to 25 km thick, and a lower layer of simatic rock, 15 to 25 km thick.

Continental drift—A theory that an original single continent, sometimes referred to as *Pangaea*, split into several pieces that 'drifted' laterally to form the present-day continents.

Continental glacier—An ice sheet that covers mountains and plains of a large section of a continent. Existing continental glaciers are on Greenland and Antarctica.

Continental shelf—Shallow, gradually sloping zone from the sea margin to a depth where there is a marked or rather steep descent into the depths of the ocean down the continental slope. The seaward boundary of the shelf is about 200 m (100 fathoms) in depth, but may be either more or less than this.

Continental slope—Portion of the ocean floor extending from about 200 m at the seaward edge of the continental shelves, to the ocean deeps. Continental slopes are steepest in their upper portion, and commonly extend to about 4,000 feet (2,000 fathoms) downward.

Contour line—A map line connecting points representing places on the earth's surface that have the same elevation. Contours represent the vertical or third dimension on a map which has only two dimensions. They show the size and shape of physical features such as hills and valleys.

Core—The innermost zone of the earth. Surrounded by the mantle.

Coriolis effect—The tendency of any moving body to continue in the direction in which the earth's rotation propels it. The direction in which the body moves because of this tendency, combined with the direction in which it is aimed, determines the ultimate course of the body relative to the earth's surface. In the Northern Hemisphere, the Coriolis effect causes a moving body to veer to the right of its direction of forward motion; in the Southern Hemisphere, to the left. This effect causes cyclonic storm-wind circulation to be counterclockwise in the Northern Hemisphere and clockwise in the Southern.

Crater — A roughly circular, steep-sided basin generally at the summit of a volcano with a diameter less than three times its depth.

Creep — As applied to soils and surface material, slow downward movement of a plastic type.

Crevasse — A deep crevice or fissure in glacier ice.

Crust — The outermost zone of the earth, composed of solid rock between 30 and 50 km thick. Rests on the mantle, and may be covered by sediments.

Cycle of erosion — A qualitative description of river valleys and regions passing through the stages of youth, maturity, and old age with respect to the amount of erosion that has been effected.

Datum plane — The reference surface from which all altitudes on a map are measured. This is usually mean sea level.

Deep focus — Earthquake focus deeper than 300 km. The greatest depth of focus known is 700 km.

Deep-sea trenches — See *Island arc deeps*.

Deflation — The erosive process in which the wind carries off unconsolidated material.

Deformation of rocks — Any change in the original shape or volume of rock masses. Produced by mountain-building forces. Folding, faulting, and plastic flow are common modes of rock deformation.

Delta — A plain underlain by sediments that accumulate where a stream flows into a body of standing water when its velocity and transporting power are suddenly reduced. Originally so named because many deltas are roughly triangular in plan, like the Greek letter *delta* ($\triangle$) with the apex pointing upstream.

Dendritic pattern — An arrangement of stream courses that, on a map or viewed from the air, resembles the branching of trees.

Differential weathering — The process by which different sections of a rock mass weather at different rates. Caused chiefly by variations in composition of the rock itself.

Discharge — With reference to stream flow, the quantity of water that passes a given point in unit time.

Discontinuity (within the earth's interior) — Sudden or rapid changes with depth in one or more of the physical properties of the materials constituting the earth, as evidenced by seismic data.

Discordant pluton — An intrusive igneous body that cuts across surfaces of bedding or foliation in the rocks into which it has been intruded.

Disintegration — Synonymous with *mechanical weathering*.

Distributary channel or *stream* — A river branch that flows away from a main stream and does not rejoin it. Characteristic of deltas and alluvial fans.

Divide — Line separating two drainage basins.

Drainage basin — The area from which a given stream and its tributaries receive their water.

Drift — Any material laid down directly by ice, or deposited in lakes, oceans, or streams as a result of glacial activity. Unstratified glacial drift is called *till* and forms moraines.

Drumlin — A smooth, streamlined hill composed of till. Its long axis is oriented in the direction of ice movement. The blunt nose points upstream and a gentler slope tails off downstream with reference to the ice movement.

Dune — A mound or ridge of sand piled by wind.

Dyke — A wall-like discordant igneous intrusion.

Earthquake — Waves in the earth generated when rocks break after being distorted beyond their strength.

Elevation or *Altitude* — The vertical distance between a given point and the datum plane.

End moraine — A ridge of till marking the farthest advance of a glacier. Sometimes called *terminal moraine*.

Entrenched meander—A meander cut into underlying bed-rock when regional uplift allows the originally meandering stream to resume downward cutting.

Erosional flood plain—A flood plain that has been formed by the lateral erosion and the gradual retreat of the valley walls.

Erratic—It is a stone or boulder carried by ice to a place where it rests on or near bedrock of different composition.

Eustatic change of sea level—A world-wide change in sea level produced entirely by an increase or decrease in the amount of water in the oceans.

Exfoliation—The process by which plates of rock are stripped from a larger rock mass by physical forces.

Exfoliation dome—A large, rounded domal feature produced in homogeneous coarse-grained igneous rocks by the process of exfoliation.

Extrusive rock—A rock that has solidified from a mass of magma that poured out upon the earth's surface.

Fault—A surface of rock fracture along which there has been differential movement.

Fault-block mountain—A mountain bounded by one or more faults.

Fiord—A glacially deepened valley that is now occupied by the sea to form a long, narrow, steep-walled inlet.

Fissure eruption—Extrusion of lava from a fissure in the earth's crust.

Flood basalt—Basalt poured out from fissures in floods that tend to form great plateaus. Sometimes called *plateau basalt*.

Flood plain of aggradation—A flood plain formed by the building up of the valley floor by sedimentation.

Focus—The source of a given set of earthquake waves.

Foreshock—A relatively small earthquake that precedes a larger earthquake by a few days or weeks and originates at or near the focus of the larger earthquake.

Fringing reef—A reef attached directly to a landmass.

Frost action—Process of mechanical weathering caused by alternate freezing and thawing. Expansion of water during freezing provides the energy for this action.

Geographical poles—The points on the earth's surface marked by the ends of the earth's axis of rotation.

Geological column—A chronological arrangement of rock units in columnar form with the oldest units at the bottom and the youngest at the top.

Geological time-scale—A chronological sequence of units of earth time.

Geomagnetic poles—The dipole best approximating the earth's observed field is one inclined $11\frac{1}{2}°$ from the axis of rotation. The points at which the ends of this imaginary magnetic axis intersect the earth's surface are known as the geomagnetic poles.

Geosyncline—The term refers to a basin in which progressive sinking of the basin floor is explained only in part by the load of sediments. All folded mountain ranges were built from geosynclines, but not all geosynclines have become mountain ranges.

Geyser—A special type of thermal spring which intermittently ejects its water with considerable force.

Glacier—A mass of ice, formed by the recrystallisation of snow, that flows forward, or has flowed at some time in the past, under the influence of gravity.

Gondwanaland—Southern continent thought to have broken up in the Mesozoic, the resulting fragments forming present-day South America, Africa, Australia, India, and Antarctica.

Gradation—Levelling of the land which is constantly being brought about by the forces of gravity and such agents of erosion as water at the surface and underground, wind, glacier ice, and waves.

Gradient—Slope of a stream bed.

Ground moraine—Till deposited from a glacier over the surface of the earth and forming a gently rolling surface.

Ground-water—Underground water within the zone of saturation.

Ground-water table—The upper surface of the zone of saturation for underground water. It is an irregular surface with a slope or shape determined by the quantity of ground-water and the permeability of the earth materials. In general it is highest beneath hills and lowest beneath valleys. Also referred to as *water table*.

Hanging valley—A valley that has a greater elevation than the valley to which it is tributary, at the point of their junction. Often (but not always) created by a deepening of the main valley by a glacier.

Horn—A spire of bedrock where cirques have eaten into a mountain from more than two sides around a central area.

Hot spring—A spring that brings hot water to the surface. A *thermal spring*.

Hydraulic gradient—Head of underground water divided by the distance of travel between two points.

Hydrological cycle—The general pattern of movement of water from the sea by evaporation to the atmosphere, by precipitation on to the land, and by movement under the influence of gravity back to the sea again.

Ice cap—A localised *ice sheet*.

Ice sheet—A broad mound-like mass of glacier ice of considerable extent with a tendency to spread radially under its own weight.

Infiltration—The soaking into the ground of water on the surface.

Intensity (of an earthquake)—A number related to the effects of earthquake waves on man, structures, and the earth's surface at a particular place. Contrast with *magnitude*, which is a number related to the total energy released by an earthquake.

Intermittent stream—A stream that carries water only part of the time.

Island arc deeps—Arcuate trenches bordering some of the continents. Some reach depths of 9,000 m or more below the surface of the sea. Also called deep-sea trenches or trenches.

Isoseismic line—A line connecting all points on the surface of the earth where the intensity of shaking produced by earthquake waves is the same.

Isostasy—The ideal condition of balance that would be attained by earth materials of differing densities if gravity were the only force governing their heights relative to each other.

Joint—A fracture in a rock mass where there has been no relative movement of rock on opposite sides of the fracture.

Juvenile water—Water brought to the surface or added to underground supplies from magma.

Karst topography—Irregular topography characterised by sinkholes, streamless valleys, and streams that disappear underground, all developed by the action of surface and underground water in soluble rock such as limestone.

L—Symbol for earthquake surface waves.

Laccolith—A concordant igneous intrusion that has domed up the strata into which it was intruded.

Landslide—A general term for relatively rapid mass movement, such as slump, rock slide, debris slide, mudflow, and earthflow.

Large waves—Earthquake surface waves.

Lateral moraine—A ridge of till along the edge of a valley glacier composed largely of material that fell on the glacier from valley walls.

Laterite—Tropical soil rich in hydroxides of aluminium and iron formed under conditions of good drainage.

Lava—Magma that has poured out on to the surface of the earth, or rock that has solidified from such molten material.

Levee (natural)—Bank of sand and silt built by a river during floods, where suspended load is deposited in greatest quantity close to the river. The process of developing natural levees tends to raise river banks above the level of the surrounding flood plains.

Limb—One of the two parts of an anticline or syncline on either side of the axis.

Lithification—The process by which unconsolidated rock-forming materials are converted into a consolidated or coherent state.

Load—The amount of material that a transporting agency, such as a stream, a glacier, or the wind, is actually carrying at a given time.

Loess—An unconsolidated, unstratified wind deposit of small, angular mineral fragments, usually buff in colour. Characteristically able to stand on very steep to vertical slopes.

Magnetic pole—The north magnetic pole is the point on the earth's surface where the north-seeking end of a magnetic needle free to move in space points directly down. At the south-magnetic pole the same needle points directly up. These poles are also known as *dip poles*.

Magnitude (of an earthquake)—A number related to the total energy released by an earthquake. Contrast with *intensity*, which is a number related to the effects of earthquake waves at a particular place.

Mantle—The intermediate zone of the earth. Surrounded by the crust, it rests on the core at a depth of about 2900 km.

Mass movement—Surface movement of earth materials induced by gravity.

Meander—A turn or sharp bend in a stream's course.

Mechanical weathering—The process by which rock is broken down into smaller and smaller fragments as the result of energy developed by physical forces. Also known as *disintegration*.

Medial moraine—A ridge of till formed by the junction of two lateral moraines when two valley glaciers join to form a single ice stream.

Metamorphism—A process whereby rocks undergo physical or chemical changes, or both, to achieve equilibrium with conditions other than those under which they were originally formed. The agents of metamorphism are heat, pressure, and chemically active fluids.

Meteoric water—Ground-water derived primarily from precipitation.

Monadnock—A hill left as a residual of erosion, standing above the level of a peneplain.

Moraine—A general term applied to certain landforms composed of till.

Mountain—Any part of a landmass that projects conspicuously above its surroundings.

Mountain chain—A series or group of connected mountains having a well-defined trend or direction.

Mountain glacier—Synonymous with *alpine glacier*.

Mountain range—A series of more or less parallel ridges, all of which were formed within a single geosyncline.

Mudflow—Flow of a well-mixed mass of rock, earth, and water that behaves like a fluid and flows down slopes.

Neve—Granular ice formed by the recrystallisation of snow. Intermediate between snow and glacier ice.

Normal fault—A fault in which the hanging wall appears to have moved downward relative to the footwall. Opposite of a thrust fault.

Nuee ardente—A French term, meaning "hot-cloud," applied to a highly heated mass of gas-charged lava ejected more or less horizontally from a volcanic vent on to an outer slope down which it moves swiftly, however slight the incline, because of its extreme mobility.

Oceanic crust—Portion of the earth's crust composed of a layer of simatic rock.

Orogeny—Process by which mountain structures develop.

Outwash—Material carried from a glacier by meltwater, and laid down in stratified deposits.

Oxbow lake—An abandoned meander isolated from the main stream channel by deposition, and filled with water.

P—Symbol for earthquake primary waves.

Paired terraces—Terraces that face each other across a stream at the same elevation.

Pangaea—A hypothetical continent from which all the other continents are supposed to have originated through a process of fragmentation and drifting.

Pediment—Broad, smooth erosional surface developed at the expense of a highland mass in an arid climate. It is underlaid by bevelled rock, which is covered by a thin layer of gravel and rock debris. The final stage of a cycle of erosion in a dry climate.

Pedology—The science that treats of soils—their origin, character, and utilisation.

Pelagic deposit—Material formed in the deep ocean and deposited there.

Peneplain—An extensive, nearly flat surface developed by subaerial erosion, and close to base level, toward which the streams of the region are reducing it.

Perched water table—The top of a zone of saturation that overlies an impermeable horizon above the level of the general water table in the area. It is generally near the surface, and frequently supplies a hillside spring.

Permeability—For a rock or an earth material, the ability to transmit fluids. Permeability is equal to velocity of flow divided by hydraulic gradient.

Physical geology—The branch of geology that deals with the nature and properties of materials composing the earth, the processes by which they are formed, altered, trans-ported, and distorted, and the nature and development of landscape.

Piedmont glacier—A glacier formed by the coalescence of valley glaciers and spreading over plains at the foot of the mountains from which the valley glaciers came.

Pirate stream—One of two streams in adjacent valleys that has been able to deepen its valley more rapidly than the other, has extended its valley headward until it has breached the divide between them, and has captured the upper portion of the neighbouring stream.

Plateau basalt—Basalt poured out from fissures in floods that tend to form great plateaus. Sometimes called *flood basalt.*

Playa—The flat-floored centre of an undrained desert basin.

Playa lake—A temporary lake formed in a playa.

Pluton—A body of igneous rock that is formed beneath the surface of the earth by consolidation from magma.

Plutonic igneous rock—A rock formed by slow crystallisation, which yields coarse texture.

Porosity—The percentage of open space or interstices in a rock or other earth material.

Pot-hole—A hole made in the solid rock of a stream channel by sands, gravels, and boulders caught in an eddy of turbulent flow and swirled for a long time over one spot.

Precipitation—The discharge of water, in the form of rain, snow, hail, sleet, fog, or dew, on a land or water surface.

Primary wave—Earthquake body waves that travel fastest and advance by a push-pull mechanism. Also known as longitudinal, compressional, or P-waves.

Push-Pull wave—A wave that advances by alternate compression and rare faction of a medium, causing a particle in its path to move forward and backward along the direction of the wave's advance.

Pyroclastic rock—Fragmental rock blown out by volcanic explosion and deposited from the air. Includes bomb, block, cinder, ash, tuff, and pumice.

Radial drainage—An arrangement of stream courses in which the streams radiate outward in all directions from a central zone.

Rectangular pattern—An arrangement of stream courses in which tributaries flow into larger streams at angles approaching 90°.

Recumbent fold—A fold in which the axial plane is more or less horizontal.

Rejuvenation—A change in conditions of erosion that causes a stream to begin more active erosion and a new cycle.

Relief—Difference in elevation between the tops of hills and the bottom of valleys.

Reverse fault—A fault in which the hanging wall appears to have moved upward relative to the footwall. Also called *thrust fault*. Contrast with *normal fault*.

Ring dyke—An arcuate dyke with steep dip.

Ripple marks—Small waves produced in unconsolidated material by wind or water.

Roche moutonnée—A sheep-shaped knob of rock that has been rounded by the action of glacier ice. Usually only a few feet in height, length, and breadth. A gentle slope faces upstream with reference to the ice movement. A steeper slope attributed to plucking action of the ice represents the downstream side.

Rock flour—Finely divided rock material pulverised by a glacier and carried by streams fed by melting ice.

Run-off—Water that flows off the land.

S—Symbol for secondary earthquake wave.

Saltation—Mechanism by which a particle moves by jumping from one point to another.

Salt dome—A mass of salt (NaCl) generally of roughly cylindrical shape and with a diameter of about 1.5 km near the top. These masses have been pushed through surrounding sediments into their present positions.

Sandstone—A detrital sedimentary rock formed by the cementation of individual grains of sand commonly composed of the mineral quartz.

Scale (of a map)—The ratio of the distance between two points on the ground and the some two points on the map.

Schist—A metamorphic rock dominated by fibrous or platy minerals. Has schistose cleavage and is a product of regional metamorphism

Sea cave—A cave formed by the erosive action of sea waves.

Secondary wave—An earthquake body wave slower than the primary wave. A *shear, shake,* or *S-wave.*

Sedimentary rock—Rock formed from accumulations of sediments, which may consist of rock fragments of various sizes, the remains or products of animals or plants, the product of chemical action or of evaporation, or mixtures of these. Stratification is the most characteristic feature of sedimentary rocks.

Seismic seawave—A large wave in the ocean generated at the time of an earthquake. Popularly, but incorrectly, known as a *tidal wave.* Sometimes called a *tsunami.*

Seismograph—An instrument for recording vibrations, most commonly employed for recording earth vibrations.

Seismology—The scientific study of earthquake vibrations.

Shake wave—Wave that advances by causing particles in its path to move from side to side or up and down at right angles to the direction of the wave's advance, a shake motion. Also called *shear wave* or *secondary wave.*

Shallow focus—Earthquake focus within 60 km or less of the earth's surface.

Shear wave—Wave that advances by shearing displacements (which change the shape without changing the volume) of a medium. This causes particles in its path to move from side to side or up and down at right angles to the direction of the wave's advance. Also called *shake wave* or *secondary wave*.

Sheeting—Joints that are essentially parallel to the ground surface. They are more closely spaced near the surface and become progressively farther apart with depth. Particularly well developed in granitic rocks.

Sial—A term coined from the symbols for silicon and aluminium. Designates the composite of rocks dominated by granites, granodiorites, and their allies and derivatives, which underlie continental areas of the globe. Specific gravity is about 2.7.

Sima—A term coined from the symbols for silicon and magnesium. Designates a world-wide shell of dark, heavy rocks. The sima is believed to be the outermost rock layer under deep, permanent ocean basins, such as the mid-Pacific.

Sinkhole—Depression in the surface of the ground caused by the collapse of the roof over a solution cavern.

Slump—The downward and outward movement of a rock or unconsolidated material. Also called *slope-failure*.

Snowfield—A stretch of perennial snow existing in an area where winter snowfall exceeds the amount of snow that melts away during the summer.

Snowline—The lower limit of perennial snow.

Soil—The superficial material that forms at the earth's surface as a result of organic and inorganic processes. Soil varies with climate, plant and animal life, time, slope of the land, and parent material.

Solifluction—Mass movement of soil affected by alternate freezing and thawing. Characteristic of saturated soils in high latitudes.

Spheroidal weathering—The spalling off of concentric shells from rock masses of various sizes as a result of chemical weathering.

Spit — A sandy bar built by currents into a bay from a promontory.

Spring — A place where the water table crops out at the surface of the ground and from where water flows out more or less continuously.

Stack — A small island that stands as an isolated, steep-sided rock mass just off the end of a promontory.

Stalactite — A cylindrical or conical deposit of minerals hanging from a cave roof. It is generally composed of calcium carbonate.

Stalagmite — Column or ridge of calcium carbonate growing upward from the floor of a cave, and caused by water dripping from the roof.

Stratification — The structure produced by the deposition of sediments in layers or beds.

Stream capture or *Piracy* — The process whereby a stream rapidly eroding headward, cuts into the divide separating it from another drainage basin, and provides an outlet for a section of the stream in the adjoining valley. The lower portion of the partially diverted stream is called a *beheaded stream*.

Stream terrace — A surface representing remnants of a stream's channel or flood plain when the stream was flowing at a higher level. Subsequent downward cutting by the stream leaves remnants of the flood plain standing as a terrace above the present level of the stream.

Striation — A scratch or small groove made by glacial action. Bedrock, pebbles, and boulders may show striations produced when rocks trapped by the ice were ground against bedrock or other rocks. Striations along a bedrock surface are oriented in the direction of ice flow across that surface.

Strike — The direction of the line formed by intersection of a rock surface with a horizontal plane. The strike is always perpendicular to the direction of the dip.

Subsequent stream — A tributary stream flowing along beds of less erosional resistance, parallel to beds of greater resistance. Its course is determined subsequent to the uplift that brought the more resistant beds within its sphere of erosion.

Subsurface water — Water below the surface of the ground. Also referred to as *underground water*, and *subterranean water*.

Superimposed stream — A stream whose present course was established on young rocks burying an old surface. With uplift, this course was maintained as the stream cut down through the young rocks to and into the old surface.

Surface wave — Wave that travels along the free surface of a medium. Earthquake surface waves are sometimes represented by the symbol L.

Syncline — A fold in stratified rocks in which the limbs dip downwards towards one another from opposite directions. It is the reverse of an *anticline*.

Talus — A slope formed by an accumulation of rock fragments at the foot of a cliff or ridge, generally formed by frost action. The term 'talus' is often used to mean the rock debris itself.

Tarn — A lake formed in the bottom of a cirque after glacier ice has disappeared.

Terminal moraine — A ridge or belt of till marking the farthest advance of a glacier. Sometimes called *end moraine*.

Terrace — A nearly level surface, relatively narrow, bordering a stream or body of water, and terminating in a steep bank. Commonly the term is modified to indicate origin, as in *stream* terrace and *wave-cut* terrace.

Terrigenous deposit — Material derived from above sea level and deposited in deep ocean. Example: volcanic ash.

Texture — The general physical appearance of a rock, as shown by the size, shape, and arrangement of the particles that make up the rock.

Thermal gradient — The rate at which temperature increases with depth below the surface of the earth. A general average is about 30°C increase per kilometer.

Thermal spring — A spring that brings warm or hot water to the surface. Sometimes called *warm spring* or *hot spring*.

Thrust fault — A fault in which the hanging wall appears to have moved upward relative to the footwall. Also called *reverse fault*. Opposite of *normal fault*.

Tidal current — A water current generated by the tide-producing forces of the sun and moon.

Tide — Alternate rising and falling of the surface of the ocean, or the earth itself, in response to forces resulting from motion of the earth, moon, and sun relative to each other.

Till — Unstratified and unsorted glacial drift deposited directly by glacier ice.

Tombolo — A sand bar connecting an island to the mainland, or joining two islands.

Topographic deserts — Deserts deficient in rainfall either because they are located far from the oceans towards the centre of continents, or because they are cut off from rain-bearing winds by high mountains.

Traction — The process of carrying material along the bottom of a stream. Traction includes movement by saltation, rolling, or sliding.

Trellis pattern — A roughly rectilinear arrangement of stream courses in a pattern resembling a garden trellis.

Tropical deserts — Deserts lying between 5° to 30° north and south of the equator.

Truncated spur — The bevelled end of a divide between two tributary valleys where they join a main valley that has been glaciated. The glacier of the main valley has worn off the end of the divide.

Tsunami — A large wave in the ocean generated at the time of an earthquake. Popularly, but incorrectly, known as a tidal wave. Sometimes called *seismic sea-wave*.

Tundra — A stretch of arctic swampland developed on top of permanently frozen ground. Extensive tundra regions have developed in parts of North America, Europe, and Asia.

Ultimate base level — Sea level, the lowest possible base level for a stream.

Unconformity — A buried erosion surface separating two rock masses, the older of which was exposed to erosion for a long interval of time before deposition of the younger.

Underground water—Water below the surface of the ground. Also referred to as *subsurface water*, and *subterranean water*.

Uniformitarianism—The concept that the present is the key to the past. This means that the processes now operating to modify the earth's surface have also operated in the geological past, that there is a uniformity of processes past and present.

Unpaired terrace—A terrace formed when an eroding stream, swinging back and forth across a valley, encounters resistant rock beneath the unconsolidated alluvium and is deflected, leaving behind a single terrace with no corresponding terrace on the other side of the stream.

Valley glacier—A glacier confined to a stream valley. Usually fed from a cirque. Sometimes called *alpine glacier* or *mountain glacier*.

Varve—A pair of thin sedimentary beds, one coarse and one fine. This couplet of beds has been interpreted as representing a cycle of one year, or an interval of thaw followed by an interval of freezing in lakes fringing a glacier.

Ventifact—A pebble, cobble, or boulder that has had its shape or surface modified by wind-driven sand.

Velocity of a stream—Rate of motion of a stream measured in terms of the distance its water travels in a unit of time.

Volcanic ash—Dust-sized pyroclastic particle.

Volcanic eruption—The explosive or quiet emission of lava, pyroclastics, or volcanic gases at the earth's surface.

Volcano—A landform developed by the accumulation of magmatic products near a central vent.

Water gap—The gap cut through a resistant ridge by a superimposed or antecedent stream.

Water table—The upper surface of the zone of saturation for underground water. It is an irregular surface with a slope or shape determined by the quantity of ground-water and the permeability of the earth materials. In general, it is highest beneath hills and lowest beneath valleys.

Weathering — The response of materials that were once in equilibrium within the earth's crust, to new conditions at or near contact with water, air, or living matter.

Wind gap — The general term for an abandoned water gap.

Yardang — A sharp-edged ridge between two troughs or furrows excavated by wind action.

Zone of aeration — A zone immediately below the surface of the ground, in which the openings are partially filled with air, and partially with water trapped by molecular attraction.

Zone of saturation — Underground region within which all openings are filled with water. The top of the zone of saturation is called the *water table*. The water contained within the zone of saturation is called *ground-water*.

INDEX

INDIA—THE LAND AND PEOPLE SERIES

<u>BOOKS PUBLISHED</u>

FLOWERING TREES
by DR. M. S. RANDHAWA

An interesting account of flowering trees of India. There are 55 illustrations including 14 in colour. Demy 8vo. Pp 188.

Popular Edn. Rs. 6.50   Library Edn. Rs. 9.50

ASSAMESE LITERATURE
by PROF. HEM BARUA

A comprehensive history of Assamese Literature. Demy 8 vo. Pp. 288

Popular Edn. Rs. 5.00   Library Edn. Rs. 7.50

SNAKES OF INDIA
by DR. P. J. DEORAS

All about snakes found in India and their identification. It contains nearly 75 illustrations, including 16 in colour. Demy 8 vo. Pp. 164.

Popular Edn. Rs. 6.50   Library Edn. Rs. 9.50

LAND AND SOIL
by DR. S. P. RAYCHAUDHURI

Types of soils in India, their utility, causes for deterioration and improving the quality. There are 38 plates, 26 diagrams and 5 maps. Demy 8vo. Pp. 192

Popular Edn. Rs. 5.25   Library Edn. Rs. 8.25

COMMON TREES
by DR. H. SANTAPAU

Deals with the common trees found in India. There are 34 illustrations, 12 in colour and 17 diagrams. Demy 8vo. pp. 148

Popular Edn. Rs. 5.25   Library Edn. Rs. 8.25

MINERALS OF INDIA

by MRS. MEHER D.N. WADIA

(Edited by DR. D. N. WADIA, F. R. S.)

An account of the mineral wealth of India with 10 monochrome plates including 1 map. Demy 8vo. Pp. 216

Popular Edn. Rs. 5.25   Library Edn. Rs. 8.25

DOMESTIC ANIMALS

by SHRI HARBANS SINGH

An account of the various types of domestic animals and country's livestock. There are 20 monochrome plates. Demy 8vo. Pp. 176

Popular Edn. Rs. 4.25   Library Edn. Rs. 8.00

FORESTS AND FORESTRY

by SHRI K. P. SAGREIYA

Contains all the relevant information about forests and forestry in a simple language for the non-specialist. It has 33 illustrations, 5 maps and one chart. Demy 8vo. Pp. 236

Popular Edn. Rs. 5.25   Library Edn. Rs. 8.50

GEOGRAPHY OF RAJASTHAN

by DR. V. C. MISRA

A geographical survey of the State of Rajasthan with its various aspects. There are 27 illustrations and 24 maps. Demy. 8vo. Pp. 204

Popular Edn. Rs. 6.00   Library Edn. Rs. 8.25

GARDEN FLOWERS

by Dr. Vishnu Swarup

Gives full information about garden flowers with their distinguishing characteristics with 58 illustrations including 16 in colour. Demy 8vo. Pp. 284

Popular Edn. Rs. 6.00   Library Edn. Rs. 9.50

POPULATION

by Dr. S. N. Agarwala

A systematic investigation into the causes of populations growth and its influence on human welfare. There are nine diagrams. Demy 8vo. Pp. 156

Popular Edn. Rs. 3.75   Library Edn. Rs. 7.00

NICOBAR ISLANDS

by Kaushal Kumar Mathur

An interesting account of the land and people of Nicobar Islands touching almost all aspects of their life. There are 12 illustrations and a map. Demy 8vo. Pp. 260

Popular Edn. Rs. 5.50   Library Edn. Rs. 9.00

VEGETABLES

by Dr. B. Choudhury

Deals with the vegetables grown in India from common man's point of view. It has 25 illustrations including 8 in colour. Pp. 218.

Popular Edn. Rs. 5.25   Library Edn. Rs. 8.25

COMMON BIRDS

by DR. SALIM ALi and MRS. LAEEQ FUTEHALLY

Gives important characteristic of the common birds of India. It has 98 fine colour plates. Demy 8v. Pp. 132

Popular Edn. 9.00   Library Edn. 15.00

ECONOMIC GEOGRAPHY OF INDIA

by PROF. V. S. GANANATHAN

Gives a comprehensive view of the economic geography of the country analysing the trends and achievements in the different fields. Contains 20 illustrations, 19 maps and twenty tables. Demy 8'v. Pp. 156.

Popular Edn. Rs. 5.25   Library Edn. Rs. 8.25

BOOKS IN PRESS

GEOLOGY OF INDIA
by DR. A. K. DEY

MEDICINAL PLANTS
by DR. S. K. JAIN

FLOWERING TREES
by DR. M. S. RANDHAWA
(Second Revised Edition)

BOOKS UNDER PREPARATION

AGRICULTURE

1. FOOD CROPS   Dr. M. S. Swaminathan,
                                 Director,
                                 Indian Agricultural Research
                                 Institute, New Delhi.

2. FRUITS

Prof. Ranjit Singh,
Horticulture Division,
Indian Agricultural Research
Institute, New Delhi.

3. CROP PESTS

Dr. S. Pradhan,
Head of the Division of Entomology,
Indian Agricultural Research
Institute, New Delhi.

4. PLANT DISEASES

Dr. R. S. Mathur,
Plant Pathologist to Government of
U.P., Kanpur.

ARCHAEOLOGY

5. THE STORY OF INDIAN
ARCHAEOLOGY

Dr. Y. D. Sharma,
Superintending Archaeologist,
Archaeological Survey of India,
South-West Circle, Aurangabad.

BOTANY

6. COMMON INDIAN FERNS

Dr. S. C. Verma,
Department of Botany,
Punjab University, Chandigarh.

7. SHRUBS AND
CLIMBERS OF INDIA

Prof. M. B. Raizada,
Principal,
D.A.V. Post-Graduate College,
Dehra Dun.

CULTURE

8. TEMPLES OF SOUTH INDIA

Shri K. R. Srinivasan,
Superintendent,
Archaeological Survey of India,
Southern Circle, Madras

9. TEMPLES OF NORTH INDIA

Shri Krishna Deva,
Superintendent,
Archaeological Survey of India,
North-Western Circle, Dehra Dun.

10. MUSIC

Thakur Jaideva Singh,
Formerly Chief Producer (Music),
A.I.R., New Delhi.

11. INDIAN COINS

Dr. Parmeshwari Lal Gupta,
Patna Museum, Patna.

| 12. | URDU LITERATURE | Shri Gopi Nath Aman, Delhi. |

GEOGRAPHY

| 13. | ATLAS OF INDIA | Dr. S. P. Chatterjee, Director, National Atlas Organisation, Calcutta. |

| 14. | GEOGRAPHY OF HIMALAYAS | Dr. R. L. Singh, Prof. and Head of the Department of Geography, Banaras Hindu University, Varanasi. |

| 15. | GEOGRAPHY OF ANDHRA PRADESH | Dr. Shah Manzoor Alam, Director, Hyderabad Metropolitan Research Project, Osmania University, Hyderabad. |

| 16. | GEOGRAPHY OF BIHAR | Dr. P. Dayal, Department of Geography, Patna University, Patna. |

| 17. | GEOGRAPHY OF DELHI | Dr. M. P. Thakore, Principal, Govt. Degree College Kalkaji, New Delhi. |

| 18. | GEOGRAPHY OF GUJARAT | Dr. K. R. Dikshit, Department of Geography, University of Poona, Poona. |

| 19. | GEOGRAPHY OF MADRAS | Dr. (Miss) A. R. Irawathy, Principal, Queen Mary's College, Madras. |

| 20. | GEOGRAPHY OF MADHYA PRADESH | Dr. K. N. Varma, Prof. and Head of the Department of Geography, Government T.R.S. College, Rewa, M.P. |

21.	GEOGRAPHY OF MAHARASHTRA	Dr. C. D. Deshpande, Director of Education, Government of Maharashtra, Poona.
22.	GEOGRAPHY OF MYSORE	Dr. L. S. Bhat, Professor, Indian Statistical Institute, (Regional Survey Unit) Yojana Bhawan, New Delhi.
23.	GEOGRAPHY OF ORISSA	Dr. B. N. Sinha, Head of the Department of Geography, Karnatak University, Dharwar.
24.	GEOGRAPHY OF THE PUNJAB	Dr. O. P. Bharadwaj, Principal, Government College, Ludhiana.
25.	GEOGRAPHY OF HARYANA	—do—
26.	GEOGRAPHY OF WEST BENGAL	Prof. S. C. Bose, Department of Geography, University of Gorakhpur, Gorakhpur (U.P.)
27.	GEOGRAPHY OF UTTAR PRADESH	Dr. A. R. Tiwari, Head of the Department of Geography, St. John's College, Agra.
28.	GEOGRAPHY OF ASSAM	Dr. H. P. Das, Professor and Head of the Department of Geography, Gauhati University, Gauhati.
29.	INDIA—A GENERAL SURVEY	Dr. George Kuriyan Formerly Professor of Geography, University of Madras, Madras
30.	GEOGRAPHY OF KERALA	—do—
31.	MEDICAL GEOGRAPHY OF INDIA	Dr. R. P. Misra, Head of the Department of Geography, University of Mysore, Mysore.

METEOROLOGY

32.	THE MOONSON AND RAINFALL	Dr. P. K. Das, Director, Meteorological Department, New Delhi.

SOCIOLOGY AND SOCIAL SCIENCES

33. GOVERNMENT AND ADMINISTRATION IN INDIA — Prof. V. K. N. Menon, Trivandrum.

34. THE STORY OF INDIA'S LANGUAGE — (Gen. Ed.) Dr. S. M. Katre, Director, Deccan College Post-Graduate and Research Institute, Poona-6.

35. PEOPLE OF INDIA — Shri Surjit Sinha, Deputy Director, Anthropological Survey of India, Calcutta.

36. LAW IN INDIA — Dr. G.S. Sharma, Director, The Indian Law Institute, New Delhi.

37. INDIAN RAILWAYS — Shri M.A. Rao, Chairman and Managing Director, Engineers India Ltd., New Delhi.

ZOOLOGY

38. INSECTS — Dr. A. P. Kapur, Director, Zoological Survey of India, Calcutta
and
Shri K. C. Pradhan Superintending Zoologist, Zoological Survey of India, Calcutta.

39. MAMMALS OF INDIA — Dr. B. Biswas, Superintending Zoologist, Zoological Survey of India, Calcutta
and
Shri H. Khajuria, Superintending Zoologist, Zoological Survey of India, Central Regional Centre, Jabalpur.

40. FISHES — Dr. (Miss) M. Chandy Principal, Miranda House, University College for Women, Delhi.

(Note: Other assignments are being negotiated with eminent authors.)